Teaching First

A Guide for New Mathematicians

© 2000 by the Mathematical Association of America (Inc.)
ISBN: 0-88385-165-2

Library of Congress Catalog Card Number 00-108054

Printed in the United States of America

Current Printing
10 9 8 7 6 5 4 3 2 1

Teaching First

A Guide for New Mathematicians

Thomas W. Rishel

Published and Distributed by
The Mathematical Association of America

The MAA Notes Series, started in 1982, addresses a broad range of topics and themes of interest to all who are involved with undergraduate mathematics. The volumes in this series are readable, informative, and useful, and help the mathematical community keep up with developments of importance to mathematics.

MAA Notes

11. Keys to Improved Instruction by Teaching Assistants and Part-Time Instructors, *Committee on Teaching Assistants and Part-Time Instructors, Bettye Anne Case,* Editor.

13. Reshaping College Mathematics, *Committee on the Undergraduate Program in Mathematics, Lynn A. Steen,* Editor.

14. Mathematical Writing, by *Donald E. Knuth, Tracy Larrabee, and Paul M. Roberts.*

16. Using Writing to Teach Mathematics, *Andrew Sterrett,* Editor.

17. Priming the Calculus Pump: Innovations and Resources, *Committee on Calculus Reform and the First Two Years,* a subcomittee of the Committee on the Undergraduate Program in Mathematics, *Thomas W. Tucker,* Editor.

18. Models for Undergraduate Research in Mathematics, *Lester Senechal,* Editor.

19. Visualization in Teaching and Learning Mathematics, *Committee on Computers in Mathematics Education, Steve Cunningham and Walter S. Zimmermann,* Editors.

20. The Laboratory Approach to Teaching Calculus, *L. Carl Leinbach et al.,* Editors.

21. Perspectives on Contemporary Statistics, *David C. Hoaglin and David S. Moore,* Editors.

22. Heeding the Call for Change: Suggestions for Curricular Action, *Lynn A. Steen,* Editor.

24. Symbolic Computation in Undergraduate Mathematics Education, *Zaven A. Karian,* Editor.

25. The Concept of Function: Aspects of Epistemology and Pedagogy, *Guershon Harel and Ed Dubinsky,* Editors.

26. Statistics for the Twenty-First Century, *Florence and Sheldon Gordon,* Editors.

27. Resources for Calculus Collection, Volume 1: Learning by Discovery: A Lab Manual for Calculus, *Anita E. Solow,* Editor.

28. Resources for Calculus Collection, Volume 2: Calculus Problems for a New Century, *Robert Fraga*, Editor.

29. Resources for Calculus Collection, Volume 3: Applications of Calculus, *Philip Straffin,* Editor.

30. Resources for Calculus Collection, Volume 4: Problems for Student Investigation, *Michael B. Jackson and John R. Ramsay,* Editors.

31. Resources for Calculus Collection, Volume 5: Readings for Calculus, *Underwood Dudley,* Editor.

32. Essays in Humanistic Mathematics, *Alvin White,* Editor.

33. Research Issues in Undergraduate Mathematics Learning: Preliminary Analyses and Results, *James J. Kaput and Ed Dubinsky,* Editors.

34. In Eves' Circles, *Joby Milo Anthony,* Editor.

35. You're the Professor, What Next? Ideas and Resources for Preparing College Teachers, *The Committee on Preparation for College Teaching, Bettye Anne Case,* Editor.

MAA Service Center
P. O. Box 91112
Washington, DC 20090-1112
800-331-1622   fax: 301-206-9789

Dedication

Clearly, every graduate student I have ever worked with has had an impact on this book, and I would like to dedicate this text to the five hundred or so who have passed through Cornell over the past nineteen years.

I hope that none of the other 499 Cornell students will mind if I do recognize one of them by name. Two years ago, Robert Battig was about to receive his PhD when he died suddenly from diabetes. John and Marietta, I just want you to know that Robert has not been forgotten.

Contents

More Advanced Topics

Professional Questions

Introduction

This is a text about teaching college mathematics.

My view is personal, informed by over forty years in higher education, about thirty of them teaching in some form or another, and almost twenty of those involved with training and evaluating teaching assistants and junior faculty. If I seem to emphasize first-and second-person narrative in my writing, it is because much of this text has come, literally, from discussion with *you,* the T.A. or junior faculty member, about the real world situations we are encountering daily in our classrooms.

At almost every juncture in the text, I emphasize nuts and bolts considerations over theory. This is not because I believe that theory does not exist or is not important, but because I think that good teaching starts with seeming trivialities — "talk loudly, write large, prepare carefully, explain a lot, be friendly." Only after we are familiar with such simplicities do we begin to feel comfortable moving into theories of learning. This last is not to say that such theories are never useful or important — if they were not useful, Mary Ann Malinchak Rishel and I would not have written the long section on how using cognitive methods can lead to better examinations. However, I do think that you, as a graduate T.A. or a young faculty member, will profit more and improve faster from short, simple, clear suggestions that have immediate and obvious impact in your day-to-day life in the classroom. If this improvement leads you to decide that you want to think more deeply about your current and future teaching, so much the better. Send me e-mail so we can talk.

Finally, let me address a very common view about the discipline of teaching; namely, as I was told again just last week, "Teaching can't be taught." Well, maybe, just maybe, **great** teaching is lightning in a bottle and can't be explained, but I claim emphatically that **good** teaching can be taught. Of course, I am biased in my view, if only because I have spent the last twenty years (roughly) trying to achieve this aim. But, in fact, I believe not only that teaching **can** be taught, but that if mathematics is to progress, it **must** be taught — to the bright young people who will carry it on after us. I hope that, by the end of this volume, you will agree with me.

So, let's stop talking and get to work...

First Steps

Types of Teaching Assistantships: Recitation, Lecture, Grading

Most teaching assignments for graduate students fall into one or another of the three categories listed in the title of this section.

Probably the most common T.A. assignment in mathematics, and the one with which the majority of the faculty began their careers, is that of recitation instructor. Those of you who have received an undergraduate degree from a large university will be familiar with the lecture-recitation format: a faculty member lectures to a large class of students two or three times a week on an assigned topic from a textbook, after which a graduate student answers questions about the lecture and discusses assigned homework problems. In this format, the lecturer decides which problems to assign and often determines the structure of the recitation. By this I mean he or she may say "Don't do all the problems; just the ones that are designated 'not to be turned in for grading.'" Alternatively, the lecturer may suggest that you begin each recitation with a couple of "example problems." Generally, however, most instructors will give you little or no advice, except to say something like "Just do a standard recitation." (For a sample "standard recitation," whatever that may be, see the later section, What Goes On in Recitation.)

Another common assignment for T.A.s is to be asked to lecture. Schools vary as to when in a graduate student's career this is to be done; at some institutions you are handed an algebra and trigonometry text and told, "Go teach this. Don't mess up!" (I won't say what I personally think of a school that puts a beginning graduate student in such a position, but it's probably pretty clear.) Other schools wait for a year or two until you have had some less demanding assignments before they ask you to plan lessons, make up your own exams, decide grading policy, and generally deal with the problems of teaching undermotivated freshmen (or worse, undermotivated seniors!) the joys of precalculus.

It is probably worth pointing out here that at some stage of your graduate career you should actively pursue a lecturing assignment, for a number of reasons:

- A graduate student who has lectured has a real advantage in the job market (see the section, Jobs, Jobs, Jobs).

- By lecturing before you take a first faculty position, you remove some of the stress over teaching that goes into the tenure-pressure.

A third common T.A. assignment is that of grading, sometimes in an elementary course, more often in an advanced undergraduate or even a graduate course. Many T.A.s describe such assignments as "easy" or "boring." While the assignments can be either or both, however, grading jobs can teach you how far you have come since the days when this course's material was a real effort. These assignments can also show you how hard it is to teach others to write clear, concise answers and proofs. A third benefit to a grading job is that you yourself can use it to review the material you may be asked on a graduate comprehensive examination. I will say more about the questions involved in grading papers later on in the section titled Grading Issues.

For now, think about:

Which type of T.A. assignment appeals to you most now? Is there one that you think you might never want to do? Do you think that your opinions might change later on in your career, or are they set in stone?

Before You Teach: A Checklist

- ❏ Do you have keys for your office or your classroom?
- ❏ Are the classrooms going to be open?
- ❏ What kinds of security are you responsible for?
- ❏ Where is your office? What is your office number?
- ❏ Can you get a desk copy of the textbook for your course?
- ❏ Can you write in the margin of the textbook? Or will you have to return the book at the end of the term?
- ❏ Where is the library?
- ❏ Where are the restrooms?
- ❏ Can you get pencils and paper? Or do you have to buy your own?
- ❏ What is the policy on making copies of exams for your class?
- ❏ Will you find chalk and erasers in the classroom?
- ❏ Are the copy room and mail room accessible during evenings and weekends?
- ❏ Do you have enough copies of handouts for your entire class?
- ❏ Where can you find the class schedule so you know where you are teaching?
- ❏ Who is in charge of the class?
- ❏ Can you get old syllabi for your class? How about last year's exams?
- ❏ Will you be using calculators in your class? If so, what type?
- ❏ Can you get an overhead projector and transparencies? Do you even want these things? How about a projector for calculators?
- ❏ How long is the semester? Is the exam schedule made up in advance?
- ❏ How many students might you expect to see in your class?
- ❏ How much grading are you expected to do?
- ❏ Can you get your teaching schedule changed easily?
- ❏ What is a typical workload for a new T.A.?
- ❏ And, where do you get your paycheck?

Day One

It is fitting that I begin writing this section now, for today is the first day of the second semester. I have just walked past a large lecture hall; the instructor is up front, animated; students are listening intently, wanting to know what is coming. For me, the irony here is that I have passed this room often during past semesters, usually observing a scant attendance of students sleeping or reading the campus news.

Day one of the semester is too important to throw away. If all we do is call the roll and send students out, what message are we sending? "I didn't really think about this class until now," maybe, or, "You don't need to be any more serious about the material than I have been just now." Yet, many instructors imply just that message by their demeanor on day one.

On the first day of class, students want to know how the course will be run: what are the major topics, why is the material relevant, and, of course, "How will we be graded?" In light of these student interests, what can be done with day one? Here are some suggestions:

- Call the roll — but don't stop here.
- Hand out, read, and answer questions about the syllabus.
- Explain how you intend to handle classes.
- Discuss the "nuts 'n bolts" of homework, exams and grading.
- Offer an overview of the course.

Now let's discuss some aspects of each of the categories above.

By the seemingly simple act of calling the roll, you signal that you want to know the students as more than just bodies occupying space. You will get to know some names, and that will make the course more "personalized." This can lead to better attendance at later classes, fewer problems like cheating (since the students feel more "invested" in the class, and since they know that you know who they are), and better course evaluations for you at the end of the course.

Handing out a syllabus is another common first day activity. If you are new to teaching, you yourself will have many questions as to how to construct such a syllabus, some of which can be answered in a later section, What Should be in a Syllabus.

Many instructors assume that students will read what is handed to them; I think this is incorrect. Every time I hand out a document, whether it be a syllabus or a homework assignment, I read it to the students. By reading through the syllabus, I allow students to ask questions that I may not have answered clearly in my text, and I also ensure that, within reason, students know what is required of them. First-time graduate students are often teaching first-time undergraduates. The undergraduates need to know how college operates: "Should I bring my textbook to each class?" "Will you collect homework every day?" "Do you answer questions during class, or do we wait until later?" "Do you grade on attendance?"

More advanced students will have questions, too. Maybe they have never had a mathematics course in college, or more likely, they just want to know what "the rules" are: "I have lots of job interviews this semester. Do you require attendance?" "Will you have answer sheets in the library, the way they did last semester?" By the way, there is nothing wrong with answering, "I don't know; I'll think about it and check with other instructors and older T.A.s and the librarian and let you know next class." Just make sure that you carry out your part of this bargain and give them a definite answer at the next class.

As to more specific comments about how class is to be handled, we will return to this topic in the section, Types of Assignments.

Students want to know whether and how often homework is going to be collected. Will you grade each problem, or only some? How will they know which of these alternatives you have chosen? Do you have an idea of how you'll assign grades to the homework? For instance, will you use a numerical system where each problem is worth, say, from zero to five points? If you know what system you and the course leader are using, now is a time you can tell the students. Similarly, you may describe when you will give exams, and whether they will occur in class or in the evening. You can also describe where the exams will be given, for instance, in a large lecture hall with 400 students, or in the classroom. You might also tell your class that "You will have ninety minute exams, and later in the semester I will show you some old exams for review."

Then you can explain what you know of the final exam and grading policies; for instance, is the final cumulative and does it take place over the same ninety minutes, or longer? Does it count for more points than the earlier exams?

There are other bits of information you should give: the names of the texts for the course, your office hours if you know them, any supplemental texts or materials you will use.

Now that you have spent about twenty minutes on the nuts and bolts of the course, it is time to turn your attention to content. What are the topics your students will be learning? How do those topics relate to other subjects they may be studying? In what ways will the material be useful "in the real world"?

Let's be more specific about details. Many of you will start teaching with a first semester calculus course. You may want to say something like this:

Calculus is usually split into two types: differential and integral. Differential calculus deals with **instantaneous** rates of change — how things change "right now," not over six years or ten miles (those are average rates of change) — not over six seconds or six one-hundredths of a second, but **right now**, this instant. We will be learning about this instantaneous change — this so-called derivative — how to find it, how to manipulate it, and how to use it in problems from physics and chemistry to business and economics. For instance, if the instantaneous change takes place over time, then this derivative is the velocity of the object that is moving, and this concept is of special interest to physicists and engineers; it is one of their tools for explaining the physical world. When Isaac Newton wrote F = ma, for instance, he was saying that forces are related to acceleration, and acceleration is a derivative — a rate of change.

Scientists are not the only people interested in calculus. Economists and business people also use the subject; for instance, the cost of doing business changes essentially instantaneously over time; this change of cost is called marginal cost. Monitoring marginal cost allows businesses to track their changes today, not over the last twenty weeks or twenty months.

Then you might go on to explain how taking a derivative requires having a function to work with, thus you will begin with a review of some continuous and not-so-continuous functions. After that, you can say that you will go on to talk about various methods of taking derivatives of more and more involved functions, and then you will discuss some applications of derivatives, such as how to maximize and minimize profits, velocities, or areas of land.

At this point, I will leave it as an exercise for you to decide what you might want to say about integral calculus and/or differential equations. Meanwhile, let's shut the door on this first day calculus class, and move down the hall to the precalculus class, where a more "activist" discussion has begun:

Instructor (I): "...and we'll also talk about functions. Maybe some of you have seen some functions, like, say, polynomials. Can you name some functions that are polynomials?"

Two students together (S_1 and S_2): S_1: "Sure. $y = ax^n + bx^{n-1} + \cdots$"

S_2: "Unh — maybe x^2?"

I: "O.K. $y = x^2$ works. It's a polynomial. Any others?"

S_1: "x^3?"

S_2: "How about $y = x^2 + x + 1$?"

I: "Yes. [Writing both polynomials on the board.] Anything harder?"

S_3: "How 'bout square root of x?"

I: [Writing $y = x^{1/2}$ on the board.] "That one doesn't work. Does anyone know why?"

[Silence. Then...]

S_1: "'Cuz 'one-half' is wrong."

I: "Good. One-half doesn't work — as a power, right? I mean, $y = (1/2)x^2$ is a polynomial, right? [Pause] So, this ½ [points to the power in $x^{1/2}$] doesn't work — I mean, it's not 'legal' for being a polynomial, although it is 'legal' for being some kind of function, yes? (This [points] is called a power, by the way, and the other is a coefficient of the polynomial. We'll define these terms pretty carefully during the course…"

[A couple of minutes later.]

I: "How about some other kinds of functions? Have any of you heard of trig functions? Can you name some?"

S_1: "Sure. $y = \sin x$."

I: "Yep, sine works. We'll study it, and the others, like cosine and tangent – and why they're all different from polynomials. 'Sine's' picture, by the way, is [Draws a sine curve on the board], right? And, it comes up in spring and pulley mechanisms, and electrical stuff, and things like that, and…."

This last instructor can teach us a lot about managing the classroom. Notice how she accepted the answer she needed to her first question, rather than going with the seemingly more complete response from Student 1, who obviously knows a good deal of the material she may be spending the semester teaching to others in the class. She also did a good job adapting to the incorrect answer "$y = x^{1/2}$" suggested by Student 3. She did so without emphasizing the student's wrong answer; in fact, she turned a common mistake into a learning experience for the entire class.

There are many good points to the classroom discussion we have just witnessed. In the interests of keeping the discussion short, let's just summarize our impression: Most people say that teaching precalculus is "boring, boring, boring," but this particular instructor doesn't make it seem so.

As exercises, think about the following two questions.

1. Which of the two methodologies described above for a first-day discussion of course material would you be more comfortable with?

2. Fill in the details of what you would say to a first semester calculus class about the topics of integration and differentiation. (Your answers may be "nothing," of course, but you should then have an explanation based on the syllabus.)

What Goes On in Recitation

One typical format for a recitation is this: The T.A. begins by asking if there are any questions on the assigned homework problems. Someone then asks to see "section 6.2, number 17." Other students chime in with "I couldn't do number 29," and "How about number 5?" Others ask for some problems from section 6.3. One fairly quiet person says "I wonder if you could do an old problem from section 6.1?" Then, for good measure, another student asks you to try one of the questions from section 6.4, the next assignment, "so we can see how they are done."

You, as the person in charge, can field questions in the order in which they occur, taking section 6.2, number 17 before number 5 from the same section, say. Or, you can ask for a list of all the problems at the start of class, collect them on the board, and do them in the order in which they occur in the textbook. The advantage of the first method is that you answer questions in the order in which they arrive. The disadvantage is that the student who couldn't do one of the easy problems may be totally at a loss as to what you are talking about when you start off with the hardest problem in the section. The second method solves the latter problem, but only at the risk of "falling behind in the material." This is a point you may not consider too important, but students always do.

A *via media* for making the best of both methodologies is to collect the questions as above. Then tell the students you will do the section 6.4 question "if there is time at the end of class." Starting with current material, do two or three of the problems from section 6.2, one or two from section 6.3, and then go back to the one from 6.1. Finally, if there is time, you can "suggest a hint to get people started" on the 6.4 exercise, which, after all, essentially no one has looked at but the one student who asked. In this way, you have emphasized current material of most interest to the majority of the class, while at the same time showing that you are willing to deal with "old and new business" as time permits. And, by giving just a hint as to how to do the new question, you allow the entire class the opportunity to puzzle out the secrets of that particular problem.

It should be clear by now that, since recitation consists mainly of discussing homework problems, you as recitation leader should show up on time and be prepared to discuss past and current assigned problems. A shocking number of T.A.s and instructors try to "wing it," often with unpleasant consequences for themselves, their students, and for their end of term evaluations. So I will say this again, with emphasis:

> A recitation instructor will show up on time prepared to discuss past and current homework problems. No excuses are acceptable; this is part of your job.

This means that you will read through all the problems the night before recitation, you will perform the required computations (yes, the chain rule is dull, and you have used it so often before, but, just when you don't prepare a set of problems because they're too easy, that's when you'll get stuck in front of your class on the day before the exam.), and you will get "the answer in the back of the book," because that's the one the students prize so highly.

Why do you want to prepare meticulously when you know this stuff so well? Because:

- People never learn course material as well as when they have to explain it to others.
- Even though you took and passed this course some years ago, that doesn't mean you can't learn from a refresher. After all, it was six years ago in high school that you took AP calculus, right?
- Textbook authors love to put "little tricks" into the exercises to keep students on their toes; these tricks can trip up unsuspecting instructors, too.
- Even a T.A. who has "done this course three times already" needs to recall where the pitfalls are placed.
- You are getting paid to do these exercises.

You can probably add one or two more well placed reasons to this list. If so, do so — and then remember those reasons when you decide to take a day off from preparing.

One final thought on this topic: Course evaluations bear out the importance of instructor preparation in students' estimations of teaching. Even those faculty who are described as "boring" and "unmotivating" usually receive overall evaluations in the B-minus to B-natural range if students say that they "can do the coursework" as shown by their being well prepared.

In this section, I have emphasized the importance of being ready to teach recitations. Preparation is important, but it isn't the only thing. For more advanced advice, see the sections on The Active Classroom and Motivating Students.

Name some of the topics you think I have slighted or ignored in the above discussion. How essential do you think they are to good recitations?

What Should be in a Syllabus

Some departments keep syllabus files, which provide a major impetus for institutional, not to mention personal, memory. Even if such a file is not readily available, you can still find out who taught your course last time, what books they used, which chapters they covered, how pleased they were with the outcome, what types of technology they used and what they thought of the students. In the unlikely possibility that the previous instructors all have retired or left town, you can get some hints and advice from members of the curriculum committee, or maybe even from the staff member who deals with the campus bookstore. If all else fails, you can look in appendices C through G for some sample syllabi of randomly chosen undergraduate courses.

Enough said about how to find old syllabi; now, what should yours describe?

First, give the name, number and section of the course. Especially if multiple sections are taught, you want to identify yours as specifically as possible. Also write days, times and room numbers on the syllabus; e.g., MWF 10–10:50, 304 White Hall. Put your name on the syllabus (some prefer "Professor A. B. C. Jones," others like "D. Smith"), your office number and hours if you know them. If you haven't decided your office hours yet, promise to write them on the board as soon as you do know them, and do so often over the next few weeks.

It is worth saying here that I am always amazed — but probably should not be — at how little verbal information is processed, and I am reminded of this fact over and over again throughout my career. ("I told the students that that topic would be covered on the exam, but they didn't listen….").

Name the required and recommended texts and readings, including edition numbers, specifying which texts are required and which are recommended. Then explain which chapters will be covered ("Thomas-Finney, 9th edition, chapters 1–7"). If you are new to teaching, you may not be sure as to which chapters are required. It is very important that you find out this information, for if students go on to the next course without having seen all of the requirements, a lot of people will be annoyed and upset — and people don't often forget what and who "caused their problems."

Also on the syllabus discuss homework, exams and grading in general; if you try to get too specific about requirements, students will come back later to tell you how you have "changed your syllabus" — "unfairly," of course. (For more details about grading schemes themselves, see the section entitled Grading Issues. For now, we will stick with what goes into the syllabus.) Will you be assigning homework by the class? By the week? The month? The entire semester? Will you collect and grade all the homework problems, or just some? If just some, will you be announcing in advance which ones you will grade? When will you collect these problems, e.g., "Right at the start of class each Monday"? Do you want the homework written out in any particular format?

Then there are exams. Do you know when they are to occur? If so, put that information into the syllabus, along with any other details you may have, such as how long the exams will be and where they will take place.

As far as grading is concerned, offer a general statement like, "...three equally weighted exams, along with a comprehensive final exam counting double [alternatively, one-and-one-half?] the value of the exams. Homework and class participation will also count about ten percent of the total grade." In this way, you offer the students a framework, while at the same time allowing yourself some leeway — what is "class participation," for instance, and how do you propose to measure it? Yet, it's logical to suggest that such participation is worth something, and you do want to have a mechanism for rewarding students who make an extra effort.

At this point, syllabi often diverge, depending on course, material and style. For instance, I have seen a few — very few, actually — faculty put a short description of their academic credentials in the syllabus. Others, especially those who are teaching in a fairly nontraditional way, will feel the need to describe the classroom situation as they see it happening. For instance, they might describe how their "project-oriented" calculus sections will work, what kinds of writing assignments they will offer in their geometry class, or how they will handle group work in their precalculus class.

Regardless of what you put into your syllabus, it would be well to remember that this document takes on the character of a contract with the students; you are telling them what you plan to do, and in turn what you expect from them. Thus it behooves you to take a little care with what you write. You might consider passing it by an older, wiser faculty member for approval.

Courses often require unplanned or unexpected changes in midstream. Most of these are acceptable to students. On occasion, however, some adjustments you understand to be minimal or benign will elicit an unexpected outburst — "Why are you canceling exam three? I was counting on that one to boost my grade! You can't do this unless the entire class agrees, you know!" And then, heaven forbid, if you decide to "take a vote" on the question, those students with higher grades plus those who just don't want to take an exam along with those who just want to get the course over with will simply outvote the three "really angry" ones who want the exam. The ultimate outcome is that you may have to end up giving an exam you hoped not to give, giving it against the express wish of the majority, and you have lost the respect of and authority over your students.

No one can avoid all difficulties or see all the possible problems about to appear. However, you need to think carefully about your syllabus before you start the semester. That, and getting input from colleagues is a strategy that will make for a more coordinated course. The outcome of such planning will then be better for you and for the students, and will make your course less work in the long run.

Some topics for you to discuss:

1. What goes into your course? What would you add to the above syllabus? Is there anything that you think should be subtracted from the syllabus, and if so, why?

2. How would you resolve the problem discussed in this section of the student who wants to take the third exam? Is he being unfair? Are you wrong for suggesting that the exam be dropped?

Lesson Planning: Survivalist Tactics

Suppose you came to town on Thursday; it was your first time at the college. Suppose further that classes begin on Monday, that you have to move into your new apartment, register for classes, wait for the cable to be connected, and — oh yes — you have to start teaching your very first class on Monday morning. For what to do on Day One, of course, you can look back to that section in these notes. But that doesn't let you off the hook that easily, because you are stuck trying to build a syllabus. And then, once you have given the students a general introduction to the course, you will have to start making up lesson plans. Further, you won't just have lesson plans for Tuesday (or, if you're lucky, Wednesday) — you have to plan an entire semester's worth.

In this section, let's consider the most basic aspects of lecturing. Later on, in sections called The Active Classroom and Motivating Students, we will look at more refined aspects of making such plans.

Once, some years ago when I was a graduate student teaching a night course in third-semester calculus, I got the twenty-four hour flu about an hour before class started. My officemate, being a very kind person, offered to substitute for me. "Just tell me which section you were supposed to do."

The next day, after I had sufficiently recovered, I asked my officemate how things had gone. "Fine," he replied, and went on to tell me how far he had gotten in the material. "But how did you prepare?" I asked. "Easy. I went in to class, announced that I was substituting for you, asked to borrow a copy of the text, and gave the students a five minute break while I looked over the author's approach to the material. Then I made up three examples of varying difficulty, and I went with it. By the way, how are you feeling?"

So there it is; a basic plan for lesson plans (a "plan for plans"), courtesy of my former officemate.

- Start by finding out what today's topic is supposed to be.
- Peruse the text to see how the author approaches the topic — this helps you preserve the same notation as the book, thereby reducing the amount of confusion in the class.
- Prepare an intuitive explanation (a "heuristic argument") as to why the topic is important, useful, and relevant.

- Next, prepare a few homework-style problems of increasing difficulty to illustrate to the students the main concepts of the section of the text.
- Allot remaining class time to answering questions or doing old homework problems.

Of course, this methodology doesn't solve all problems. If it did, teaching would be trivial. So let's discuss more fully some of the issues raised in the above outline.

One complaint often voiced is: "But I don't like the way the author does this section. Why should I encourage bad mathematics?"

Fair enough. Even though we may not have had a choice in the textbook, the students will still be using it for explanations, exercises and homework. We can offer alternative proofs or better methods, but if the students are getting their homework from the text, they would rather not have to keep "translating" from our language and symbolism to the author's. Thus we owe it to the students to at least say, "Here's how the author approaches.... An easier [more common, better, more useful, more sophisticated] way is as follows.... On the homework and tests, use whichever method you like best. I don't care as long as you get the right answer and can explain your method."

Another common objection is that we should not use "informal, intuitive argument," rather than an "honest, direct, complete proof."

This suggestion may simply be a function of audience level (discussed more fully in the section Student Types). Clearly, if you are teaching the intermediate value theorem in real analysis or topology, you will want to consider the roles compactness and connectedness play in the discussion. But, for a freshman English or biology major, some pictures of continuous and discontinuous functions that have positive y-values at $x = 1$ and negative y-values when $x = 3$ will be much more convincing than an unintelligible, unmotivated "formal proof."

This last is also not to say that you can't be lucky and draw a class of eager students in an enriched calculus program for potential mathematics majors — but now we are back to the Student Types question.

A third objection is "Why do examples? They're right there in the book."

You're right; there are worked out examples in the textbook. But, first of all, many, if not most, students don't read the book. Second, not every detail of the examples is spelled out in the author's exposition. Further, it isn't always necessary to choose the examples in the text; many instructors I know don't choose the author's exercises. Instead, they opt for a few problems "near" the assigned homework problems, telling the students, "If you understand how to do these examples I'm showing you, you'll have a great start on tonight's assignment." The underlying message is the "great motivator": "It's worth watching me do these problems, because they're like the ones you'll be trying soon."

One more objection to the proposed lesson plan is often brought up: Is the suggested allotment of time for a lecture correct? That is, how can you leave so much time for questions and homework? Don't you need all that class time to explain the details of the current topic?

This too is a reasonable objection. Different instructors find that they take different amounts of time to explain details of a lesson. Still, I try to find ways to leave time for student questions; otherwise, how do I know whether they are absorbing the material I claim to be teaching them? The best way to find out if my lecture is being received is to give the students a chance to tell me what is still bothering them. I will return to this topic again in the Active Classroom section.

Grading Issues

It goes without saying that grading can bring on problems. Many students seem to feel, as someone once suggested to me, as if they "start out with 100%, and we [faculty] must justify the removal of each individual point." At the same time, faculty sometimes take the exact opposite approach.

Grading is best treated as a learning situation for all concerned — the instructor learns how well he or she has taught the material and designed the exam, while the student learns how well he or she has absorbed the course information and studied for the exam.

In mathematics, you will usually be grading homework sets, quizzes or examinations. Another possibility is that you may grade writing assignments or class projects — and, of course, you will be involved in assigning final grades.

Homework sets are generally the easiest to grade; the assigned problems are usually well written out in the text, and the solution method is fairly clear.

A common, but not universal, technique for grading homework is to assign each problem a fixed number of points. Some graders use a two-point system, "0" for a wrong answer, "1" for OK but not complete, "2" for fully correct. After using this methodology once or twice, most graders find that it "doesn't have enough points" to properly distinguish among the variety of possible errors that a group of students can make. Students also tend to sense the same problem. Their complaint about the grading is usually to say something like, "I only got one small thing wrong, and all I got was a "1".

A "zero to five scale" is probably better:

- "0" — didn't even try the problem,
- "1" — tried, but not even close,
- "2" and "3" — various levels of somewhat valid but mistaken attempts,
- "4" — correct answer, but with some minor errors,
- "5" — the correct answer with details spelled out.

Note the last comment: Only the correct answer with details merits full credit. There will be points early in the semester when students will ask you to reconsider grades because they "got the right answer" without showing any supporting evidence as to how they did so. You can use this as an opportunity to instill good habits into the students. Explain to the questioner that one point was lost on this particular assignment for not clearly describing the method used in solving the problem. This is much easier than trying to convince the same student that he or she has lost twelve points out of twenty on the exam for an answer similar to one given on an earlier homework.

This previous paragraph points out a good general principle, both for students and assistants. Homework time should be used to instill good habits. For the student, this means writing correct, clear, complete solutions. For the instructor, it requires looking to make uniform, defensible grading with useful comments.

New T.A.s often ask how long comments on papers should be. My response is usually "Not long at all." I say this because it is fairly common for newer T.A.s to continue the solution to the problem in the margin of each student's paper exactly from the point at which the first error occurred. Students often don't read these comments; when they do read them, they often don't understand what they did wrong.

There are at least two ways to reduce the amount of commenting you need to do on homework problems. One way is to simply put an "X" mark at the place where the first error occurs, and then after all the papers have been graded, write up solution sets of the most commonly misunderstood problems for all the students. A second way is to start or finish the next class with a "couple of homework problems lots of people seemed to have difficulty with."

Quiz grading is not dissimilar to that of homework. You can use a similar point scheme, and again save some grading time by putting the answers on the board when you hand back the quiz. One difference, however, is that if you are the one writing the quiz, you may occasionally find that your question is inappropriate. Even if you are not writing the quiz, but simply (but remember, nothing is ever simple) choosing a problem from the text, you may choose one that requires a piece of information that you actually didn't lecture on. In that case, "common sense" should take precedence over pure grading issues. Did you ask a question students couldn't answer with current methodology, say? Then maybe you should give everyone "full credit" for their valiant efforts, with extra credit for the one or two who may have actually known how to solve the problem.

Exam grading is in many ways like homework, although in this case careful preparation before grading can save much time. There seem to be two models of mathematics exams: Those that are given to classes of up to thirty students, and those for five thousand (well, maybe five hundred — it just feels like five thousand). In the first case, you end up grading all problems on all the student papers. In the second, you tend to grade only one problem — but you must grade until you drop, and then get up and grade some more.

Uniformity with fairness and speed are keys to grading exams. Nothing is more disconcerting than finding at 3 a.m. that you thought you had finished grading 347 individual papers, only to find that an undetermined number of them were done incorrectly. Thus, if you are grading 500 papers, working the problem carefully yourself before grading any papers is central to uniformity. When you have a complete solution, make up a credit scheme before you grade any papers. (A sample problem solution with grading scheme is shown at the end of this section.) While you are proctoring the exam, you can show your answer and grading scheme to other T.A.s for comparison — although it doesn't hurt to remember that this will be your question to grade, so the final approach is your call, as well as being your responsibility. My point here is that, within reason, you need a grading scheme you yourself are both comfortable with and that you can defend.

As you grade the first few papers, occasionally review your scheme to see if it still seems to fit what the students actually knew and did. This review will also help avoid "grade inflation or deflation" that seems so inevitable over ten hours of work ("This is the same mistake that I've seen a hundred times now — well, this one gets a zero!")

Uniformity and fairness are related to one another. You may be a harder grader than your officemate, but if you can defend your methodology to other T.A.s and students, they will generally accept it. (Note that last "generally." Some may not; see the section Get Along with Colleagues.)

Most T.A.s see the "speed" part of "grading with speed" as being of benefit only to themselves — "I want to get this pile of papers done and out of here!" But speed with accuracy also benefits students, because they get to have their problems back while they still remember what the questions were.

To aid in speediness, try some of the following:

- Grade individual problems "backwards"; if the answer is correct, you can scan the earlier parts to see if the details are there.

- If a few students have a unique, strange method of solving a problem (this happens maybe five percent of the time), put these papers aside for a while until you can let your subconscious work on where the student's "solution" may have originated.

- Do not write long comments on the examination papers; use the advice given earlier in this section.

- Make an answer sheet to hand out to all the students. Go over the answer sheet on the day you hand back the examination copies. If students feel that they did not get graded uniformly, you can make adjustments right after class.

- Don't fight with students over problems that were obviously graded incorrectly; at the same time, don't capitulate over every request for a regrade just because it was asked for.

I often tell my students that I will take the paper back to my office to think about "what's fair and accurate," and that I will then return it at the next class. This gives me time to consider my options without haste.

If you are grading a full class of exams — for instance, the entire set of exam questions for thirty students — grade problem one for each student, then go on to problem two, etc. In this way, you will ensure more uniformity. Also, try to grade each individual problem in one sitting; take a break only after you have seen all the unique, exotic methodologies the students can come up with. (By the way, I find that I can sometimes bribe myself into grading by promising that "I'll take a break as soon as I finish these last eight copies of problem 3." Not being very bright about such matters, I'm usually able to use that argument to convince myself to work ten more minutes.)

Uniformity has other benefits. Among them: It leads to fewer re-grades, which take a lot of time. It also makes for more defensible scores, so that students consider the grading (and the grad*er*) fair.

After you have graded as many homework problems, quizzes and exams as you can stand, you will have to assign final grades. Each department of each university and college seems to have allowed its own system to evolve — and each of these systems is like each other, but not quite. For the bare-bones description of one such system, check out the grading section of What Should be in a Syllabus. Note, however, that this section is not completely forthcoming as to how allocation of final grades is done in a "standard" class. Well, let us lift the veil.

I am occasionally in charge of a large number of calculus sections; for instance 26 sections averaging 20 students each. Thus, by the end of the semester, we calculus instructors have in the range of 500 grades to assign. Assume that we give three exams during the term (these are called "prelims" where I come from), each worth 100 points. We also administer a 150 point final exam (yes, it is called a "final"); and additional materials, such as homework and quizzes, add up to 50 more points. Thus students can earn a total of 500 points. If the exam is scheduled for a Tuesday morning, we will spend that afternoon, Wednesday and Thursday grading. By late Thursday afternoon or Friday morning at the latest, each instructor will have collected finals, recorded grades, and totaled raw scores. (Of course, there are always one or two instructors who have failed to do the above; they should read the section Get Along with Colleagues.) We then have a meeting at which instructors put up the raw scores of their students. This we do in ten point intervals, from 500–491 to 210–201. Numbers below that fit into a single category of 200–0 points. See the graph below for a description.

We find the median grade (not the mean), and assign to its ten-point interval the set of last B⁻ grades. Working up and down the intervals, we then assign an "A" range, a "C' level, and a "D" range.

Interval	Total	Sum
491–500	3	3
481–490	8	11
471–480	14	25
461–470	20	45
451–460	16	61
441–450	20	81
431–440	16	97
421–430	22	119
411–420	28	147
400–410	…etc.	

Having put together a "curve" based on class scores, we now assign letter grades to each student in each section. We are not done, however. In each section there are grades that are "anomalous." Some students have one grade that is much lower than the rest, say. Others have a rising set of scores, e.g., 49, 62, 87, and 130/150 on the final, showing that they maybe have "caught on" later than others. Occasionally, students will have had a death in the family or some other personal problem. I discuss each such anomaly — about fifteen percent of the total — with the individual instructor, and we come to some sort of consensus. We seem to end up raising about half the anomalous grades, but no single grade ever goes up more than one level, e.g., from C^+ to B^-.

One of my general feelings about grading is that students always do less than or equal to their best on individual exams; but still, there must be two or three exams where they perform to expectations — theirs or mine. Further, good homework and classroom questions may show interest, but they are a precursor of good exam performance, not a substitute for that performance. And finally, I have a "thing" about the grade of A^+; I will never raise a total below 490 points out of 500 to an A^+. To my mind, an "A-natural" is a perfectly wonderful grade, and I won't apologize for giving it. An artifact of this policy shows up in one of the case studies at the end of this book.

Grading is never an easy part of the job. Maybe it might help to think of the "standing in front of the class" part of teaching as the fun part, and grading as the part you get paid for. Still, it is important to know how what you taught is coming across to students, and giving and grading exams is one of the best ways to find out.

The Semester in Five Minutes

August 27–28

You spend three hours looking for your lecturer. You meet with him or her for an hour, then you realize that you forgot to ask a really important question. When you go back, he or she is meeting with undergraduate advisees. You have to wait forty-five minutes for the answer. You go home exhausted.

August 29th or 30th

Meet your classes for the first time. Take roll. Half the class is not on the roll sheet, the other half isn't in the classroom.

Students ask lots of questions only answerable if you've been at your institution for fourteen years:

Is this the right class for me?
Are you gonna do transcendental functions?
How do I transfer out of here?
Will you sign my schedule?
Did I buy the right book for this course?
Where do I go to change my registration?
I can't make the final exam at the scheduled time. Can I have a makeup?
[Possible answers: "Maybe." "I dunno; ask me again next time." "Go to (the appropriate) office." "Not at this school." "Maybe. Our book is...." "Go to (the appropriate) office." "We have some time to figure that one out, don't we?"]

Week Two

Two new students arrive. They want you to tutor them on what they missed.

A third student keeps coming to your office for at least an hour every day for help with his homework. Meanwhile, your own first big homework set in analysis is due tomorrow.

Week Five: Exam One

Thursday night is the first exam in calculus. You have to do an extra help session on Tuesday night, 7 until 9 p.m., for some of the T.A.s sections of the course.

Fifteen minutes into the exam itself, you realize that proctoring is one of the two or three most boring things you have ever done in your life.

You spend the next two minutes making a mental calculation of how many times you will do this in your lifetime.

After the exam is over, you spend the next two days grading over five hundred copies of one problem.

Week Six

You try to catch up on the class work for your own courses, but your students keep coming to you outside office hours for regrades on various problems from the first exam.

Week Seven

You get behind in your own work, so you decide to try a new teaching strategy called "showing up unprepared." That goes so badly that you decide *never* to try that again.

Week Eight

One of your students asks when you are teaching next semester because he wants to get you again. You can't say why, but this makes you feel really good for the rest of the day.

Week Nine: Exam Two

This week is like week five, the "exam one" week. It would have gone better, but you have an analysis midterm of your own the day before your students' test, and a huge algebra problem set due two days after the calculus exam.

Instead of grading for twelve hours, it only takes you ten. And the number of regrades goes way down. But it's still too much work.

Thanksgiving

Attendance goes down drastically; students head home even though there's an exam the week they return. Later, they will say on the course evaluations that you and the lecturer "didn't motivate them" in the course.

Week Thirteen: Exam Three

Students are anxious and surly because they didn't get enough time to study. The fact that this week's exam was announced in August doesn't seem to matter, nor does the fact that they did skip six classes in the last two weeks. But it's "your fault" that they didn't know enough about triple integrals.

Week Fourteen

Break before finals. Students you haven't seen for seven weeks show up for review sessions. Afterwards, two come to ask you, "What can I do to pass this course?"

You read your course evaluations. You thought you knocked yourself out helping students; they say you're average, except for the category of "organization," where you are below average.

December 15th

Like week five, but much, much worse. You have two take home exams of your own to hand in, plus one in-class final on the day after your students' final – and you have to grade over five hundred papers again.

December 20th

You have a grading meeting with all the T.A.s and the lecturer. One T.A. forgets his grade book; you have to wait forty-five minutes to calculate the class median. Then you discover that five of your students are from one to four points below the cutoff for an A. Further, two of your class attendees are not on the roll sheets, while two other students you have never heard of are.

December 21st

As you turn in your last take-home in algebra, your most annoying student walks up to you and demands to meet with you today about the fact that he got a B+, when "I obviously deserved an A–, *at minimum*!"

January 2nd

While watching a football game, you suddenly realize, "I did it! And it wasn't that bad. And, I could do it again. But not just yet."

Cooperative Learning

There are various ways to approach the methodology called **cooperative learning**. You can suggest that students do their homework sets together. You can offer them weekly study sessions where they can sit together and work problems while you circulate through the room offering hints and suggestions as to how to solve problems.

This last is an approach Myrtle Lewin and I took a few years ago (ref. [20]). We would never pick up the chalk or use the board. Myrtle's method was to stop at a desk to ask students where they were stuck on individual problems, then to offer "nudges" as to how they might proceed on those specific exercises. My technique was slightly different: I would show them how to do the problem they were stuck on, then tell them to "try the next exercise in the book; it uses the same idea, but with slightly different numbers." Then I would walk away for a few minutes to have the students work the problem themselves so that when I returned they could explain "the next exercise" to me themselves.

In class, after a short introduction of a particular topic, you can stop lecturing so as to let students try two or three of the exercises in groups, after which you can have them present their solutions at the board.

You can make up worksheets for students to use to discover mathematical concepts for themselves — some sample worksheets are provided at the end of this section.

You can teach a project-oriented type of class, and then make up some really hard worksheets for which the students will need a few days time along with some help from you to construct solutions. Then the students can work in small groups writing up their solutions. This method of cooperative learning is very labor-intensive for all concerned, and is not one you should simply blunder into. There are books available, however, to help you with the details — see, for instance, Cohen [8], Hilbert [16], Jackson [17] and Hagelgans [14]. In appendix B, I have offered one of Matt Horak's calculus projects as a sample.

You can assign major projects (or final projects, or individual projects) in place of some exam or final. Students can then report to each other on what they have learned and they can evaluate each other's projects.

I have no doubt that you can think of two or three more ways to encourage cooperative learning in your classroom.

In addition to the question of **how** cooperative sessions can be done, there is the more interesting question of **why** you might want to do them. Faculty often express a desire to have students actively engaged in the learning process; what better way to do this than to get them to work the problems and construct the examples?

An objection that is sometimes raised to this last is, "But when six people work together, I usually can't tell which of them are really working, and which are copying." OK. And, when they hand in their homework can you tell whether they did it themselves or had someone else do it for them? When you get them working in class, you can walk around observing the dynamics of groups. You can ask questions like "Where are you stuck?" and make such comments as "When your group has a solution, I'll ask one of you [not saying which one] to present it on the board." By means of these techniques you can find out who knows the material and who needs further help — and this last is one of the cornerstones of the teaching process.

Technology

Technology is being used more often in the mathematics classroom, from low-tech aids like overhead projectors and microphones through mid-tech calculators to high-tech computers. The more time you spend in teaching, the more you will be called on to use some of these materials.

Perhaps it is just my own bias, but I find it particularly annoying when an instructor comes to class unprepared to use the necessary equipment. "Ho ho, well, I brought these transparencies, but I see they don't fit the projector." [You didn't bother to check beforehand?] "And, I can't figure how to turn it on…can anyone help me? Oh, and I see that my data disk isn't compatible with the software…and no, I didn't prepare any backups, and…" — well, you were at that talk too, so we both remember it well, right?

Rule One: If you are using technology in your class, test it beforehand. Have a backup in case the worst happens, whatever "the worst" may be.

If you can get into the room early, practice with the equipment before your talk or class. Turn it on, check the displays for visibility, set audio equipment for sound clarity without feedback, make sure computer and calculator displays are visible from the back of the room, check to see that you have the proper cables and plugs for your laptop.

Rule Two: Make sure your examples justify the technology you are using.

Why do you need a calculator with an LCD display projector just to draw the graph of a parabola? Do you have to load up Minitab or Datadesk to compute means or deviations for a sample of size six? In other words, choose your examples to fit the equipment. Let the calculator graph the function $y = \sin(x)/(1 - \cos(x))$ so that you can find all max and min for that function. Have the calculator graph $y = ax^2 + 1$ for various choices of a; then ask students to describe how changing a affects the graph. Do the same for $y = x^2 + k$ for various k.

Use Minitab to find means and deviations of census data, so as to eventually construct and test hypotheses for yourself and the students to defend or disprove.

Rule Three: Make sure that your overheads and displays "fit."

A transparency with writing too small to read may not (quite) be completely useless, but it certainly is frustrating to the audience.

It is not always possible to know how a particular room or hall is going to be configured for a talk or class, but there are many good reasons for putting less information on each individual transparency and making the size of type, font or print larger than you think you will need. The next rule will discuss more details of speaking from overheads; for now, let me continue with another "nuts 'n bolts" comment.

Another frustration for the audience that is simply solved is that of the "shrinking violet" who refuses to pick up the microphone. He thinks his mumbling is sufficient, while the audience knows that the solution is available right at the lectern, if only he would use it.

Rule Four: Realize that "teaching with technology" is not the same as lecturing.

The audience does not have time to take notes or absorb the ideas being shown on transparencies. They are barely able to listen to your presentation. Such problems occur especially in **good** talks; it can be very frustrating for a listener who thinks that he or she has just seen a remarkably good lecture but can't really reproduce any but the most minimal parts of it. Such an audience has been more entertained than taught. To alleviate this problem, you could consider bringing individual copies of transparencies and displays for handouts.

Speak slowly and allow ample time for questions while overheads are still on display; recall that all but the experts in the room need time to absorb what you are telling them. Also, do not play "peek-a-boo" by covering over parts of transparencies; this is a common practice that seems appropriate in specialist sessions at large conferences. If you don't want the audience to get too far ahead of you, put less material on an individual transparency and write larger. Another method of keeping interest is to offer people a related "exercise" at the start of your presentation that (you can claim) they will be able to solve by the end of the talk.

Rule Five: Be prepared for total system meltdown.

I once gave a lecture in Japan on the day a typhoon landed. Five minutes after I began, all the electrical systems failed. When I asked what to do, the audience said, "Just go ahead with your talk." So I used chalk, wrote large on the board and spoke loudly. Some of what I said must have gotten through, because afterward a listener came up to me and very courteously pointed out an error I had made.

Having given enough caveats as to how technology might apply, let me describe a few simple examples of situations where I have found calculators useful. In both of the examples below, the goal is to use the calculator to get the students to make intuitive guesses that can then be tested, either by further use of the calculator itself or by basic materials previously discussed in class.

In introducing trigonometric functions, ask students to use the "zoom" command to adjust the graph of the sine function. While they are doing this, ask the seemingly simple question, "What does your graph show as the largest and smallest possible values of the sine?" No doubt someone will yell out the answers, "plus and minus one," pretty quickly — perhaps because he or she has seen the graph before. You can then ask the class in general whether everyone is getting this same answer, "regardless of how much zooming you do?" (This allows the slower students to have extra time to complete the task.) Then you can ask whether plus and minus one will "always be the answer, even though you can't zoom forever?" Then you can ask whether anyone can see a way to prove the answer, by saying "How do you know this really will be true forever and ever?" Let students pause to think, then nudge them gently: "How did we define the sine? We defined trig functions by using a triangle. What does this triangle we started with have to do with what I just asked?" Then ask whether the same applies to the cosine and tangent functions, and ask them for verification of their guesses for these functions before using the calculator to graph them. When the students find that the graph of the tangent is not bounded, ask them why the tan is so different from the sine and cosine. You can then go on to whether the sine and cosine functions are really the same ("Use your calculator to graph them both; how do they differ?'), and what might be a relation between those functions and the tangent.

One more example: In a calculus class, the study of asymptotes is easier to motivate with the calculator. Before defining an asymptote, ask the students to use their graphing calculator to "look for some strange characteristics" of, say, the function $y = (x^2+1)/x$. After everyone graphs this, ask them if the function "seems to be heading in a particular direction" as it goes off the screen. And, "how many different ways does it seem to head off the screen?" "OK, as Cheri said, as x goes to zero, and as Dave pointed out, as x 'gets really big.' Any others?" Eventually, students will discover that they should look at the function as x goes to zero through positive and negative values and then consider what happens as x "goes to infinity through positive and negative values." One way to get them to perform this analysis through a combination of intuition and experiment is to next ask them to graph $y = x+(1/x)$, then to "naively" ask them how the graphs compare. Once they have gotten used to using the calculator to analyze the function, you are ready to ask "what happens to the $(1/x)$-term as x goes to the various special values we have identified as important?" At this point, you can offer precise definitions of horizontal and vertical asymptotes, and move quickly on to finding them — after all, the students have already seen a well-chosen example.

If you find yourself in a situation where you need to use a large number of calculator and computer applications in your classroom, check out selected articles in Hagelgans [14] or Karian [18].

In closing this section, let me say that, as we use technology more, we will need to think carefully about how it affects what we teach and how we test. One of the questions students always ask, for instance, is "Will we be using our calculators on the exam?" We should ask ourselves what we should teach differently, what we should no longer teach, and what we should not teach with technology. Our answers to this question will determine the amount of technology we use and the ways that we test.

Writing Assignments

The first question I am usually asked about writing assignments in mathematics is: "What kind of these writing things can I possibly use for my mathematics class?" I always respond, "Small assignments that fit your mathematical curriculum." Of course, I don't always know what "your mathematical curriculum" means in various contexts, but that doesn't mean that I can't give you some general advice.

Here are some small writing assignments I have used successfully in my mathematics classroom.

Put a supply of 3×5 index cards in the back of the lecture hall for students to write questions about the topic. Answer the best or most frequently asked questions at the start of the next class.

Ask an occasional verbal quiz question in class: "What's so 'fundamental' about the fundamental theorem of calculus?" "Describe one application of today's topic." Then put one of these questions on your next short quiz.

Ask the students to end their solution of a mathematical exercise with a verbal description of the real-world implications of their answer.

Have the students write out "for their roommate who had to miss class" a description of the topics covered since the last exam, along with why those topics might be important or useful.

None of the above assignments takes a long time to construct, nor is it difficult to grade. Yet each enhances the students' awareness of the usability of the classroom material. Further, each asks the students to think a bit more holistically and carefully about the somewhat deeper meanings of the materials they are studying.

It is also possible to construct much more involved writing assignments. Of course, the above are only a small sampling of the possibilities of writing assignments in mathematics. For lots more, check Countryman [9], Meier-Rishel [22], or Sterrett [27].

The other question I tend to get about writing is "How can I grade these things? I'm not that good as a writer myself." My response to this is, "Grade for content — for the mathematical aspects: Does the paper make sense? Is there a solid argument?" If not, find the first place in the paper where the discussion seems to go astray, and just start asking questions. "What do you mean here? Are you saying [this], maybe, or [that]? Think it over, come talk it over with me if you like, then rewrite it if you wish so as to give me a sense of what you mean." In this way you are giving the student a chance to ruminate more fully about the mathematical content of the question rather than about the grammar.

Of course, grammar is important in that it affects the quality of the argument, but it should not be the defining aspect of the paper you are having the students write. By grading for content you are making the mathematical reasoning central to the topic, and ultimately that should be what you are after.

If you do decide to incorporate more challenging written work into your course, you should be aware of some of the difficulties of doing so. Among the pitfalls of written assignments are the following:

- Unfocused assignments ("Write five pages about Newton and Leibnitz") are easy to construct, but hard to recover from.
- Grading is labor-intensive.
- Students will have many questions about "why we are writing in a math class."

I think written work is wonderful, in that it gets to the center of "real mathematics," what's important about it, and why we do it. Try some writing assignments, but first, check out the references above. I guarantee from personal experience (as described on page 3 of reference [22]) that they will save you much time and pain.

Making Up Exams and Quizzes

Making up exams is both an art and a science. If you do it properly, you get an honest appraisal of your students' understanding of the course, as well as the material and approach you have taken. At the same time, by constructing good exams, you avoid the pitfalls that make examinations time consuming to grade and difficult because of post-exam complaints. If you don't do it properly...well, you can probably guess what I'm about to say.

So what are some of the steps you can use to avoid pitfalls?

First, make a list, for yourself and for the students, of the topics you have covered since the last exam. If some of these topics are too time-consuming or not interesting enough to test, say so. If you feel you need to test one of the time-consuming topics, e.g., Newton's method, or Riemann integrals evaluated by summing and then using induction, you can consider testing them by assigning a special overnight take home project.

Now that you and the students know which general topics are to be tested, it is time for you to decide, without the students' help of course, how many and what kinds of problems to include in an average examination time period.

Let's say you have ninety minutes. I sometimes tell students that I try to design a one-hour exam and then give them ninety minutes to do it. This rather meaningless bit of information seems to relax them. Generally speaking, stress reduction before the exam is not a bad idea; there is a difference between making an honest and fair, yet difficult, exam, and making one that is simply filled with tension.

Suppose you have decided on a five question exam, based on the fact that there were seven major topics since the last test, and one of those is easy enough to skip, while a second can be embedded in a later, more important topic. Make about forty percent do-able by anyone who stayed awake long enough to watch you show some examples on the board. (This is one of the reasons I don't want to pass students who cannot get a 40% average on my exams. See the section on Grading for details.) The forty percent do not have to be "just like trivial homework," by the way; you might split some of your five problems into easy, moderate and difficult sections, thereby spreading the "easy stuff" around the exam.

Now you have sixty percent of the test left for more challenging material. Half, or a bit more than that, can be **similar to** some of the more interesting examples and homework problems — the types of problems that make students think — but this group had a chance to do that thinking last week while they were doing their homework exercises. I never give the students assigned homework problems on the exams, by the way, although I do know some people who do. I just feel that using homework problems as exam questions often makes the students feel that the instructor didn't really put an effort into the preparation.

Assuming that about twenty percent of the exam is still to be constructed, it's now time for you to think of a more challenging question — or parts of questions. Now is the time to think, "What is the essence of the material I have been teaching for the last four weeks, and how can I ask the students to show whether they have absorbed that essence?" This does not necessarily mean asking them to formulate a proof; rather, it should indicate that you could quiz them about some fundamental points that you have been making repeatedly during your excellent lectures. One effect of putting such questions on the exam is to increase attendance at the rest of your excellent lectures — "Wow! If I go to class, it might help my grade on the next prelim!"

For many more details on how to make examination questions that hit the mark, try the section Using Cognitive Models to Make Appropriate Problems.

Let me say a bit more about finding challenging problems. Early in my career, I used to expend enormous amounts of energy trying to fashion a problem that would force students to use current knowledge to discover something new. For instance, I might be inclined to write the equivalent of, "You've seen exponential growth. Well, now I'll ask you to find out about logistic growth all on your own." These well-meaning attempts almost always turned out very badly. The "numbers" would turn out to be too messy, and the concepts were too far from the students' current awareness. Further, thirty minutes or so was simply too little time for serious thought. So eventually I came to the realization that at best I could formulate a couple of problems that proceed from easy to difficult, with the difficult part counting maybe only five points. ("You couldn't get that part? Well, good thing it was only worth five points. OK, let me show you how…")

How do I do this? Glad you asked. Let's go back to the "exponential growth into logistic growth" problem. I split it into four parts, each worth five points:

In problem four, you found the rate of growth of a strain of bacteria. Now let's suppose that the bacteria are growing in a lab on a circular Petri dish whose area is 5 cm^2. Thus it is fair to assume that the area, A(t), covered by bacteria in the dish at any time t is governed by the equation

$$dA/dt = k(5 - A(t)).$$

a) If you know that $A(0) = 1$ and $dA/dt = 0.2$ at $t = 0$, what value do you get for k? Is this k value positive or negative, and what does it tell you about dA/dt?

b) Next, writing $\dfrac{dA/dt}{5 - A(t)} = k\, dt$

for your value of k, solve this equation for A(t).

c) Your solution in part b) will have an arbitrary constant in it. Calling that constant D, find its exact value.

d) Using your final solution to part c), make a reasonable argument that $A(t)$ is never larger than 5. What is your reasoning for this?

Notice that the above is still not an easy problem. It wasn't supposed to be. However, the first part should be manageable for any student who understands what you have taught about exponential growth and decay. Part b) is harder, of course, except that you have already separated the variables in the equation the students have to solve. Even if students found a wrong answer to b), you can still grade part c) as if b) were correct. Thus they can still receive credit for part c) without getting very many points for b) at all — although they do have to get "some kind of reasonable answer" for b). That leaves part d). It's not easy, "but hey, at least it's only a five-pointer, right?" If you now design one more problem with a "hard five-pointer" as part d), you are done. On this exam, it will be easy to get at least 40%, the average should be around 70 or 75%, and more than 90% shows that the students have truly learned.

Before moving on, let me make a comment about classroom quizzes: I tend to make them relatively easy. For instance, if I lecture on the chain rule on Friday, and maybe I've shown the students how to find the derivative of $\sin^2(3x)$, I might then ask them to use the last five minutes of class to find the derivative of $\cos^3(2x)$. Once the students see that the quizzes are reasonably easy, they have incentive to come to class and listen carefully to what I am teaching. Further, the quiz is then easy for me; I can sometimes finish grading it in the fifteen minutes between classes, if no one stops me to ask questions.

The Active Classroom

Show up early, maybe by five minutes. Say hello. Cheerily. Start handing out old homework or new handouts. Hand them out by calling out names; this will help you remember students' names.

Ask a general question, like "How's it going?" Or, "Was the homework too hard this time?" If the response is "I couldn't do number seventeen," say, "OK, I'll do that one on the board when class starts." If it's "Yes, the homework was too long," then tell them, "OK, I'll do some at the beginning." If you're in charge of a recitation and not lecturing, you can ask if the lecturer is up to date on the syllabus — you may well know the answer to this question, but at least you will elicit a response. This is preferable to telling the students where they're supposed to be in the text and which homework you'll be discussing today. By this time, more students are filtering into the classroom, and you can bring them into the same pre-class conversation.

If the students want to talk about their flu, the previous class, or last night's basketball game, that's fine — until the prescribed time for your class to start. Then say, "Well, it's about time to start. Did anyone have a homework question, or something from the last lecture that you didn't understand?" Or tell them, "Jenny said she couldn't do number seventeen, so I promised I'd start with that one. Did anyone have a question before that?" Suppose no one does. Ask Jenny to remind everyone what question seventeen says — that way she can talk — then ask all the students present if "anyone has an idea how to start the problem." If no one says anything, don't just start solving it; offer a hint, like: "…this is a section on parametrically defined functions; what might that have to do with the problem?" At that point, someone usually suggests, "Well, I started with the formula for 'parametric derivatives.'" Respond, "Right. That's the one that goes $dy/dx = (dy/dt)(dt/dx)$, just like the chain rule, right? So how does that fit the problem?" In this way, you are getting the students to tell you what they know, not just about this problem, but also about their comprehension of the recent material from the course.

There are a number of general ways to keep the classroom active: ask leading questions — ones whose answers are not simply yes, no, or "square root of two." When a topic depends on some earlier concept, ask the students to provide the earlier information and formulas so as to show you what they remember. Once you show how to do one problem, choose a similar one and ask students to work on it communally. Then, when they have all had a chance to begin solving it, go to the board and write down what they tell you is the method of solution.

You can also tell the students a bit about the history of the topic or one application of it, and then ask them to bring in more of the history or another application for the next class. This will allow you to start off the next class with "what you have found out." Don't rush through your own answers as if time were the enemy. Give everyone an opportunity to think of whether they understand your calculations and whether they need to ask about the seemingly trivial steps you thought too easy to write down — "There you wrote '2+1,' then over there you wrote '3,' why?"

Every topic was new to each of us at some point; we had to think hard about what made it work. Then when we found out, we began to think it was trivial. But it isn't — neither for the new student nor for the person who didn't see it well the first time out. So we should give everyone a chance to ask all the questions — the smart ones, the wrongheaded ones, the ill-thought out ones, the ones we should have asked the first time we saw the material. (See "What Was That Question Again?" for more.) If we can set up a classroom atmosphere where our students can ask all these questions, then we will be a long way toward being a "good teacher," whatever that concept may ultimately mean.

A further comment on the topic of questions: Larry Sowder reminds me about the concept of **wait-time**, a good one to know about. When we are asking questions in the classroom, we need to give students a few seconds to think out their responses. Too often we mathematics instructors worry that the classroom will fall quiet, yet that is what students often need to shape an answer to a complex question. I know from personal experience in mathematics and writing classes that allowing time for a response to develop can be crucial in getting the quality discussion that we need for serious learning to take place. If we want to know what is on the students' minds, we must give them some room to tell us. Wait-time, i.e., just standing and anticipating, can allow this room.

This has been only a minimal presentation — a first-case scenario — of methods for making a classroom more responsive. More interesting and advanced techniques include the use of worksheets and cooperative strategies like having students work together. Students can also make presentations of work they have done: both small, like individual problems, and large, like final projects.

As you get further into this topic, you will want to consult such references as Bonwell [4], Cohen [8] and McKeachie [21] for more advanced suggestions.

"What Was That Question Again?"

When you lead recitations, you will find that you open yourself to all sorts of questions. This situation is one of the most anxiety-producing ones in teaching; "I have absolutely no idea what they will ask. How can I handle that?"

Let's examine some of the types of questions you will be called upon to answer:

- The standard question.

An example: "Can you do number twelve?" If you prepared before going to class, you can even answer, "Sure." Just make sure that you then do it.

- The question that makes no sense.

Everyone asks such questions on occasion; resist the impulse to put the person down. Instead, think about how to turn the question into a good one, maybe by responding with, "Maybe what you are asking is…?"

Of course, it is also possible that the listener asked a meaningless question because what you thought was a perfectly clear explanation was opaque to him or her. Or else he or she was daydreaming through part of your previous discussion. In any case, you now have been given an opportunity to reinforce points you thought that you had made earlier.

- The silly question.

Don't make a big deal of it. Act as if it's an honest question. Answer it quickly, then move on.

You will occasionally have a student who seems to specialize in silly questions. Other students will roll their eyes as soon as they see his or her hand go up; resist the impulse to "side with" the others by smiling, joking or answering with a smirk on your face. Such behavior on your part is simply unprofessional, even if you know that some of the students are going to downgrade you on evaluations for your "allowing too many stupid questions."

- The unintelligible question.

You might simply say, "I don't quite understand. Could you rephrase that?" Or, "…Are you asking about…?" Then try to reshape the question into something sensible.

   Alternatively, you can ask someone else to try to rephrase the question.

- The "challenge to your authority" question.

I often get these in first semester calculus. "Let's see if he knows what they taught me in my last week of intensive calculus at my high school." Or, "Let me ask him how to do the hardest problem in this section, even though it wasn't assigned for homework."

   I answer these questions slowly and carefully, if I can. If I don't remember the answer, I will respond, "That wasn't part of the assignment, but I'll be glad to show you in the next class." Then I make sure to do so. I resist the impulse to turn the question back on the student by asking, "Did **you** try it? Then what's the answer?" This last might set up an adversarial situation where you are either perceived as knowing the solution but unwilling to show it to the students, or as being someone who isn't really open to answering student questions.

- The "good question."

Hooray! A good question. Say, softly, honestly, "That's a good question." Then answer it. By recognizing good questions publicly, you encourage more of them.

- The question you don't have any answer for.

This is everyone's nightmare, and this nightmare will sometimes come true. So what. Just respond, "I don't know." Then ask the audience what they know about the topic. You might just learn something new. Remember, anyone can ask anyone else a question they can't answer.

   On the topic of questions and answers, I am reminded that for some years I have had a large cartoon poster on the back of my office door. A large beaked avian in a dress — "Ms. Bird," perhaps — is standing amid a circle of cute, fuzzy, small animals, who are looking wide-eyed at Ms. Bird as she intones, "There is no wrong answer, Malcolm, but if there were, that would be it." Of course, I have never said this in class, but once or twice I have thought it.

   Questions and answers are an integral part of learning. Our method of handling them is important to our effectiveness in our teaching, and ultimately in our careers. It behooves us to get used to them, to think about them, to encourage them, and to enjoy what they can teach us about ourselves. Sometimes we will even give an answer that surprises us with how much we actually know!

Motivating Students

Too many faculty interpret the word "motivating" as "pandering"; dressing up as Isaac Newton, say, telling silly jokes that are out of character, or giving out A's as if they were jellybeans. Now, far be it from me to claim that I've never told silly jokes, and I don't give out A's like jellybeans, but I have given out Pringles potato chips to illustrate hyperbolic manifolds, and...but I digress.

To me, motivating means addressing the history, culture, and usefulness of mathematics.

You don't have to get a second bachelor's degree in history to insert a bit of information into your calculus class about Newton and Leibnitz, or about Bishop Berkeley and his feud with Newton over infinitesimals. You can also spend a few minutes reading up about Euler's treatment of exponentials, Cauchy and Weierstrass on limits, and Bolzano about continuity. There are a number of references you can use for this material, for instance, Boyer [5] and Kline [19]. For a more advanced approach, try Edwards [13].

Cultural aspects of mathematics are also related to the history. Students enjoy hearing about the ancient Greek approach to infinity, and how it would have affected their willingness to accept the eighteenth and nineteenth century approaches to calculus, infinity and the infinitesimal. Further, the fact that such ideas continue to be questioned and refined into the twentieth and twenty-first centuries makes the students feel that their own skepticism about these concepts is relevant and valuable.

Students are also highly interested in how mathematics applies to their own fields of interest. Here, the principle of "Show, Don't Tell" takes over; start a section on second order linear ordinary differential equations with a model of a shock absorber from a car. Discuss the principle of damped oscillation. Then derive the differential equation for the model, discussing possible benefits and shortcomings of the assumed linearity of the system of equations. Once you have solved the system, don't stop there — discuss the meaning of the various constants as they apply to the comfort levels of the rides of individual automobiles.

The same principle applies to using Fourier series in solving the heat and wave equations, to using linear algebra in describing inventory control, to exponential functions in drug prescription, and to...but you get the idea. If you can't think of examples, just look at some of the harder problems in your current textbook; chances are that there are some good applications there.

In closing, recall that students are always asking for motivation; you are likely doing the same with respect to your first-year analysis course. If you are skeptical of what I just said, simply take note of the number of times you hear — or, in your own analysis class, you *think* — that famous question, "What's this good for?"

How to Solve It

One of the ways in which you can be helpful to your students is to offer general suggestions as to how to solve the types of mathematical problems they will be seeing throughout the semester.

Many years ago, George Polya wrote a book titled *How to Solve It* [25], in which he addressed the same question. Many people have used Polya's model since then (only a few with attribution). Polya suggests the following. To try to solve a mathematical problem:

1. Read the problem.
2. Read the problem again.
3. Draw a picture or diagram.
4. Find and label the unknowns — what you are looking for.
5. Find and label the known quantities.
6. Write down all the formulas and relations between the known and unknown.
7. Solve the problem.
8. Check the answer.

And here I might add a suggestion that Polya does not offer:

9. Think about how you might generalize the problem.

In his book, Polya shows a number of individual problems — geometry problems, word problems and related rates problems from calculus, and others — that he solves by using his methodology. Many calculus texts, for instance, Stewart [28] and Thomas-Finney [29], do the same in their discussion of word problems. Instead of my taking up space showing how they do this, I will just recommend that you take a look at these books for details.

Let me make a few suggestions about how you might approach the teaching of such difficult topics as word problems and related rates problems for the students:

- Make people comfortable — don't make time an enemy.
- Suggest "special cases" to try.

- Praise — not inordinately, but do praise — those who get the answers.
- If appropriate, ask the students how the students might generalize the problems.

Exercise:

Choose two problems from the textbook you are using next semester. Solve these problems slowly and deliberately using Polya's method – no shortcuts allowed! Does his method fit these problems? Is the fit perfect, just adequate, or not at all? (For instance, people often complain that "a picture just isn't needed for this problem.") How would you modify Polya's approach to fit your problems?

Course Evaluations

No doubt you have been on the student side — the "giving side" — of course evaluations. Now you will see the "taking side."

Course evaluations can be extremely useful in telling you how your individual class of students has perceived your teaching during a specific semester. Did the students see you as "organized"? Even if neither they nor anyone else can tell you exactly what "organized" means, the students have an opportunity to offer an opinion.

Were you "helpful"? Does that mean, "Did you answer questions without insulting the students' intelligence?" Or does it mean that you had lots of office hours, even though most students never came? Or, that, heaven forbid, one afternoon you showed them a "preview copy" of the exact same exam as the one administered that evening? Now, that last would be "helpful" — but not in the sense that a good instructor would like to see.

Were you "knowledgeable" about the material? Of course, you could be successfully completing a course in complex analysis with a grade of A+, and still have the students in your calculus section saying that you weren't knowledgeable.

In view of all the above skepticism, why do we subject ourselves to the student evaluation process?

Well, first of all, because the process does have uses other than the ones just discussed. Take, for instance, the question of "knowledge." If you know lots about functions of several complex variables yet can't give an intuitive response to the question, "Why does the ratio test work?" then of course your calculus students are going to see you as someone who doesn't know much about calculus. ("He's really a nice guy, but...") Alternatively, if your response to the question about the ratio test is to give a rigorous proof of the test, then the students are likely to give you high marks for knowledgeability — and low ones for helpfulness. ("She knows a lot of math, but she can't bring it down to our level.")

As to the question of "organization," this one is tricky. I have personally thought a lot about what it means, because I am consistently rated lower in this category than any other in my over thirty years of college teaching. I believe that when students talk about organization they seem to mean, "He has a plan in his head as to where we'll be at the end of each class, he tells us what that plan is, and he gets there almost every time." I must admit that, if this last is the students' "definition," then I don't conform to their ideal. Instead, I am willing to take questions at (almost) every opportunity; I am happy to revisit earlier concepts if students show that they don't know them; I sometimes make up more than one lesson plan in my more "nonstandard" courses, and then let the students' questions and interest dictate which one I use on a particular day. In return for this last, I occasionally begin class by outlining where we have been, and I do periodic reviews to show the students where we have come to.

I also take some comfort from the fact that one of our college's teaching award winners once told me, having seen my evaluations, "Don't worry, Tom, I always get low marks for 'organization,' too."

Student course evaluations are thus useful, without being a complete determiner of teaching ability. They tell us what the students expect of us. They teach us something about the expectations of our audience. Maybe most importantly, they allow us to find out our own classroom goals, and how these goals conform to or conflict with the ones enumerated on our evaluation forms.

In short, we need to know how we are being evaluated, where those evaluations go, and what each of the qualities listed on the evaluation form has to do with our approach to teaching.

At Cornell, we give a "nuts 'n bolts" evaluation form to all T.A.s and faculty. They are asked to hand out and collect this form very early in the term, usually around week three, but they are specifically encouraged not to turn it in to any official or semiofficial entity in the department. The function of this evaluation is to let the instructors find out "how I'm doing" in various categories, from "Do I speak loudly enough," through "Do I give enough time for questions," to "Are my answers intelligible." The full form is given in appendix A.

Get Along with Colleagues

One of the major pieces of advice you should take to heart from this entire volume is embodied in the title of this section: Get along with your colleagues.

When you are told to come to the "calculus one" meeting, do so. Grade in a timely fashion, and do it in such a way that others will not have to field two-hundred student complaints.

Do your share of the "busywork" involved in administering the course; offer to give occasional makeups; to run off five hundred copies of exams; to teach once or twice for a sick colleague. Show up for office hours; don't leave it to the other T.A.s to offer excuses for you and have to your students in your place.

Be nice to people, even if they aren't nice to you — who knows who they are, or what kinds of problems they may be having at the time. And, if they **really** aren't nice, then at least be formal and professional. You have every right to choose your friends, but colleagues are more like family — you have little or no choice in the matter. If you really can't stand someone, ask yourself why. If you think you have a good reason, fine; chalk it up to experience, and move on to get the job done as quickly as possible so as to be out of the way.

Don't speak badly to students about your fellow T.A.s, about faculty or about administrators. As a friend of mine said the other day, "Oh my goodness. I didn't realize that that person I was complaining to about the dean was his spouse!" If you have a **professional** problem with a colleague or co-worker, take the problem to a supervisor — if that person is trustworthy. If not, try your graduate student director or the chair. Say something like, "I don't want to cause a problem or get anyone into the middle of an argument with another T.A., but something has come up about [for instance] someone maybe ignoring some possible cheating on the last exam, and I need to talk it out."

By the way: Yes, I have seen a (very) few T.A.s who were successful in the classroom, but who were so difficult to deal with as colleagues — always arriving late, leaving all their T.A. duties to others, skipping classes, etc. — who were told to leave. So "brilliance" is no guarantee of support for a teaching assistant. And, believe me, it usually gets even more difficult for an uncooperative faculty member. So learn to be cooperative now, or expect to suffer a lot more for it later.

I have also seen a number of T.A.s and faculty who are "selectively nice." If a tenured faculty member is asking them for a favor, that's fine, but not a secretary.

(You have seen this too, where a faculty member treats you badly because you're "just a T.A.") Please don't be like this. In many ways, the staff runs the university. They were at their desks before the chair became chair, and they will be there when the chair has gone back to being a lowly tenured professor. They know how to cut corners, and they can be helpful to people who are courteous — and coldly uncooperative to those who are not. More to the point, they too just want to be treated like human beings, just as T.A.s do. So treat them that way.

'Nuff said.

How to Get Fired

- Act as if you don't have a "real job." It's "just a T.A."
- Don't show up for class. Several times. Without an excuse.
- Be insolent to faculty (especially your advisor), the students and the staff members.
- Call in sick every Monday. Leave for "The City" on Thursday afternoon.
- Never plan what you are going to do in class — this stuff is too easy anyway.
- Make it obvious that research is everything; you are going to solve a great problem and join one of the top departments where you will be asked to teach only one graduate course a term.
- Skip office hours. Your officemates can take care of any of the students who'll come by.
- Make it clear from the start that you don't intend to do anything extra — in fact, you won't do anything that you don't get a salary for. And, you only do that under duress.
- End all your classes early. Can't do this, you say? Too many questions? Simple to solve; just belittle the students who ask them — that'll ease up on class time.
- Leave for vacations, breaks, and end of term early. Aruba awaits!
- Don't hand in grades on time. Got some graduating seniors? So what! They didn't like you anyway.
- Offer "grades for favors" — only "jokingly," of course.
- Show up at undergrad parties. They're so much more fun, anyway. Drink a lot. Leave at 2 a.m. with one of your students.
- Tick off the T.A. supervisor. He isn't a real mathematician, anyway. He stopped doing research about the time you were born.

Of course, you won't do any of the above — you're too well trained for that.

What is a Professional?

The first time you step in front of a class, you cross an invisible line. You don't see it, but the students do; you are no longer one of them. That's why they look at you quizzically when you ask, "What should we do today?" They also don't appreciate your "little jokes" about exam grades. And, when you write a "cute" comment on their homework about how "this work is more like high school stuff," they see the comment as acerbic, and they let you know.

A professional is one who speaks for and has responsibilities to the discipline he or she is teaching and to the other practitioners of that discipline. Some of these responsibilities have been described in the section called Get Along with Colleagues, but not all. There is more to being a professional than speaking courteously to an officemate, as important as that is.

You have responsibilities to students:

- Don't discuss their individual grades in public, and don't publicly compare the students to each other. It is one thing to say, "You're a very strong student"; quite another to comment, "I thought that Joe would be better than you [or vice versa], but...."

- We have all met people who are very likeable, but favoring them with "hints" or "extra help" that others don't get is not fair.

- Socializing can lead to difficulties, even in the most benign situation — see Case Study V for an example. So, if you know deep down that you are not going into a "benign" situation, do not participate. A night of binge drinking with your undergraduate class is "definitely contraindicated," as a friend once said.

- If you are not sure how much fraternization to have with students (after all, we don't want to be totally standoffish), ask trustworthy colleagues and faculty for their advice.

- Be careful the kinds of jokes and comments you make in front of students, who can be sensitive in very unusual ways. For instance, I once teased a student who knew an arcane fact about Galois theory that he "must be reading the same kind of weird stuff that I am." When he obviously bristled, I had to apologize to him for my comment.

You will also have responsibilities to the faculty and other T.A.s:

- Do not insult or belittle others' teaching styles, or their approach to research. For instance, in a discussion of methodology, "Here's how I teach word problems" is clearly more tactful and better received than "Students tell me they don't like the way you do that topic." And, you don't need to tell your officemate that Professor Jones "can't be very competent, since he's still writing papers on...."

- If you have an honest disagreement with a colleague, keep it on a professional level: "I really think that problem might be too hard for these students," said directly to Professor Jones, is a professional comment. You may be right, you may be wrong, but at least you have had your say. The alternative of going to your officemate to gripe that "Ole Jonesy's just trying to nail as many freshmen as possible," is maybe true, but not a professional alternative.

- Pitting a class against every other instructor's is not professional. The fact that "My class had a 73% average, but Joe's was 67%" does not make anyone a better instructor. They may have overlooked the information that their class met at 11 a.m., while Joe's was right after lunch. Then there was also the fact that they "asked" two students with low test scores to switch out of their section after the first exam.

- Similarly, good instructors don't sit in the department lounge bragging about how much their course evaluations are better than others'. If someone wants to make an honest comparison of his or her evaluations, certainly no one has to lie, but professionals should also remember that there are many factors involved in various ratings of classes, students and even T.A.s. For instance, is it really true that someone once passed out donuts on evaluation day and then told the class that his job was on the line? Well, that method seems to have worked!

Most importantly, T.A.s have responsibilities to mathematics itself:

- Prepare the material. Read up on it (Yes, even "precalculus" has a history). You needn't be a cheerleader, but you should be ready to make an honest reply to "Why do we need to know this?"

- Show some interest in your teaching assignment, and in mathematics in general. If you can't find any reason for teaching that is more compelling than drawing a paycheck, is this really the way you want to spend the next forty years of your life?

Just as no one can ever know all of mathematics, no one ever knows all it takes to be a "professional." But, through a combination of talking to trusted colleagues, thinking before acting, and using common sense, we can avoid most pitfalls. If it feels wrong and sounds wrong, act carefully, because it likely *is* wrong.

More Advanced Topics

Teaching Methodologies
for Various Types of Classrooms

Without trying to be exhaustive in my list, let me describe a few of the teaching methods you may be called on to use, among them:

- Lectures
- Socratic Dialogue
- Guided Discussion
- Student-Guided Recitation

Each of these is probably well known to you, except maybe for the Socratic dialogue.

Each method has positive and negative aspects. For instance, lectures impart lots of information in a short amount of time; in the proper hands they can be organized well; and they make good use of the expertise of the lecturer. On the other hand, students can easily "nod off" literally or figuratively in lectures, and information imparted is not necessarily information received.

Socratic dialogue is often touted as an active, open form of learning that gets students involved in the educational process. In this method, the instructor usually teaches by asking questions for which the students are then to provide answers. On the other hand, if not carefully organized and monitored, such discussion can lead nowhere. It is also often "falsely democratic" in that a few speakers can dominate discussion, either crowding out other viewpoints or allowing for participation by only a few.

Guided discussion can usually have a more formal structure than the Socratic model, especially when the discussion leader uses information sheets or reading lists. Handled properly, such guided discussion can achieve the objective of finding out what the student knows. Yet students and faculty sometimes complain that such a technique isn't "fast enough" in imparting knowledge. Better prepared students, especially, often object to having to wait for others who "just don't get it."

Then there is "recitation," or student-guided learning. This methodology makes maximum use of the student and of the text, putting the "burden of proof" (not to mention "burden of effort") on the students. But it doesn't necessarily make effective use of the expert, and if guided discussion operates slowly, this method can really operate slowly. On the other hand, say those who advocate this technique, once students do "get it," there is no doubt they have it — whatever "it" is. A final argument usually offered against student-guided learning is that it can miss the most salient items involved in a course.

Finally, there is the mixed approach, which uses all of the above; ten minutes of lecture, followed by guided discussion, ending with a worksheet.

Regardless of the methodology we use, we need to ask ourselves: What is the goal we want the students to achieve, and what is the best methodology for achieving that goal?

Lesson Planning

Let's consider planning from a variety of viewpoints, first, as a teaching assistant, or maybe as an instructor in, for example, calculus, differential equations or topology, or finally in a "discussion" situation.

As a T.A., while doing homework problems before class, think about:

- Where is the "trick," and will it recur in other problems?
- How does the problem fit the topic being taught?
- Will a related problem be coming up later, perhaps one that is an extension of the current example?
- Have the students seen a similar problem or method before?
- Is there some other "point of interest" in the problem?

Also as a T.A., you may be called on to discuss:

- A "three-minute synopsis, without proofs or additives, of the topic we're working on."
- A review of topics since the last exam, or possibly for the next prelim.
- Some shortcuts or related methods, if relevant.

Some pitfalls T.A.s can experience:

- Running recitation as if it were a "better lecture than the lecture."
- Putting down certain problems or answers as too easy.
- Introducing a competition with other sections, where your students are yours, and others are "the enemy," real or perceived.
- Not coordinating with the lecturer, so that students feel that they are being asked or shown different things by you than by the instructor.
- Showing open distaste in class or office hours for some of the topics and methodologies used in lecture.

Generally speaking, students just want to get through the course with a good grade and go on to what's important — to them. (But don't give up, I'm not being completely cynical; let me finish…) They will accept, for the most part, work that is relevant to their goals, and their questions will reflect those goals: "Why is this important?" "Will this be on the exam?" You, for your part, should see both these questions as fair at any time in the course, and should be prepared, within reason, to answer them. Possible answers to the first question: "It's used later, in…." "There are engineering (business, economics, architectural) applications, and if you learn about this technique, it will make you better in that field." "The author needs it later in the chapter (or in the text), when we solve…." And the last "fair" answer: "I'm really not sure. Let's see if we can find out why the author and instructor want us to do this."

If you think about the question of what makes the topic relevant while you are preparing your recitation at home, you will be ready to answer most of the questions that come up in class. Further, you will be active in your preparation, which will make you more interesting to the students, and your material more interesting to all of you. You'll eventually become the kind of instructor the students inadvertently praise: "I didn't think I'd like the material or the course, but he/she showed me why it was useful. I still don't like it that much, but now I see why it's important."

Problems of and with Students

Chances are, if you are a sensitive, caring instructor, students will begin to see you as a "lifestyle advisor." A typical first reaction is to feel honored — but then an almost immediate response sets in; "How can I give advice to this person — or anyone, for that matter?"

The vast majority of student problems are not so serious, and you can deal with them fairly easily:

- "My goldfish died. Do I have to take the exam?"

"Well, I can understand that you can get attached to a pet, and I guess I can give you a makeup, but that exam would have to be harder because you would have had a chance to see tonight's exam. Since you already did the studying for the test, maybe it'd just be easier to take it?"

- "My grandmother died. Do I have to take the exam?"

"Well, you'll probably have to prepare to go home and all that. I can certainly give you a makeup after you return. If you think it might be easier to take the exam tonight, you can just show up, and if you don't come tonight, I'll just assume that you'll be taking the makeup at a later date. I'll do whatever's best for you, and I'm sorry to hear about your loss."

In the first situation above, I am making a strong suggestion, and any normally intelligent student will see the wisdom of taking it. Of course, he or she might really be broken up about the death of a goldfish ("But I've had Sleepy since I was twelve!"). But if the student must go ahead with his or her decision rather than taking my advice, then he or she must accept the consequences. I, as instructor, am absolved from the responsibility of having "forced my will" on this poor student. "Well, I'm sorry you failed the makeup, but I did warn you about what might happen if you took it." Outcome: The student was offered a chance to think like an adult, and rejected it.

In the "death of the grandparent" case, I am again leaving the choice up to the student, but this time I am not implying any "penalties." I emphatically do <u>not</u> get into any discussion of whether the grandparent (parent, uncle, second cousin, etc.)

has died — I don't ask for "proof." To me, there are two possibilities. In one case, the student is upset and doesn't need to be challenged. On the other hand, in the event that this is the sixth grandparent of this student who has died in the three years he has been at the school, then the student still has a problem, only this problem is of a different sort.

If you do find out later that the second student has been using "death in the family" excuses a lot, you might want to suggest that he see a counselor or examination specialist to learn how to cope with examination stress.

The above analyses also apply to such common situations as breakups with significant others, the "three exams in two days" phenomenon, and the "field hockey road trip" model. I consider the "significant others" problem reasonably serious, and usually adopt the "grandmother" approach to this one. As to the "three exams" problem, I'm much less sympathetic with that. "Sorry, but it must be the same for lots of the students in the class — and you do have a week to study for the exams." Then I continue, "The exam will be harder, and I couldn't give you more than one extra day." One of the main reasons that I am harsher in this situation is that, as soon as I give this one student more time to study, thirty-four others will be along with the same reasoning. And if I try to accommodate all of them, then most of the thirty-four will also have problems with the makeup date, etc. Then the grades will not correlate well between the original exam and the makeup, and that will lead to even greater inequities.

On a lighter note, students are apt to ask some really rather bizarre questions:

- Do I have to come to class? ("Only if you want to pass.")
- Will I have to buy the book?
- Will I have to bring the book?
- Are you sure you're the instructor? You're too young to be teaching us. (Or, as another one continued, "…because professors dress better than that.")
- I wasn't here yesterday. Did we do anything important?
- Could I copy your notes after class? I don't have time to take my own.
- Could you slow down? I can't write that fast.

I have been asked all the above, although it has been a while since someone told me I was too young to be the professor.

In the case of your being surprised by a particular question that you haven't thought of, rather than give an immediate reply, you may want to think about it for a day or two. Tell the student you will respond by e-mail as soon as you can, and then go ask someone you trust how he or she would handle the situation. This avoids the problem of making a bad decision on Tuesday and then having to either live with it or "rescind your ruling" on Wednesday. (Still, rescinding a bad ruling is better than causing real inequities over the long run.)

One more general statement about making decisions: Over the course of your teaching career, you will be called upon many times to decide in a fair, quick and accurate manner on a matter of some importance to a student or group of students. At first, this process can seem daunting, but after a while, you will have seen almost all the types of questions you will be asked. While this experience can make most of the decisions easy, some will never come smoothly, and just when you think you know how all this is done, you will make a blunder that will make you question your own intelligence — if not your sanity. The only thing you can do in such a situation is admit your mistake and go on to try to learn from it. In the main, all you can do successfully is try to be fair and honest to all the students, to your colleagues, to the department, to mathematics, and especially to yourself. The Case Studies section at the end of this book is designed to assist you in getting into the mindset for making reasonable decisions.

If a serious problem does occur, do not feel that you cannot ask the proper authorities to step in. Of course you are an intelligent person and a trained mathematician — and that's the point; you are trained as an intelligent mathematician, not as a counselor or therapist. When someone comes to you and says, "I'm afraid I'm suicidal," how should you respond? How about: "Thank you for coming to talk to me about it. It's pretty obvious that this causes you some pain, and I'm glad you're willing to speak to someone about it. I'd like to help you — would you mind if I called the university counseling service for you? I think they can provide some real support."

No one can give you perfect advice as to how to solve every problem that might occur. But if you use some common sense, don't panic, get help when necessary, and generally do your best, that's all that anyone can expect of you.

Student Types: Who is the Audience, Anyway?

The audience is important. Know, as far as you can, the motivation and interests of the group you are teaching.

Are they future engineers? Then "pure theory" is not always appreciated, or necessary. For this group, it helps to have a few mechanical or electrical applications for them to chew on.

Are you talking to pre-meds? Then they are also likely to be taking lots of biology and chemistry courses, and would appreciate hearing how mathematics is applicable to these topics. You could do problems related to bacterial growth, for instance, but you could also model drug dosage problems, spread of disease questions, and applications to heart pumping problems. If you don't know anything about these models, then you might start your classroom explanation with, "I don't know that much about the biology or engineering involved. So, if you could help me out, I'd appreciate it. Meanwhile, I'll show you a differential equation that models a heart pump."

Precalculus students are usually encouraged to hear that "this algebra and trig you are learning will show up a lot in calculus," but they are more convinced if you tell them about sine waves in music, heat exchange or building earthquake- proof buildings. You shouldn't necessarily try to show the details; you might not know them all yourself. Your job is to teach the precalculus. But at least you will be giving the students a small glimpse of a possible future.

On the other hand, some years ago I tried to show a class of sophomore engineers how electrical circuits could be modeled by differential equations. The student response was, "No! Don't show us! We're sick of the electrical stuff." So sometimes the "audience" you think you will have is not the one that actually shows up.

Sometimes instructors interpret the statement "consider the audience" as meaning "pander to the audience" or "only teach the fun stuff," whatever that may be. I am definitely not suggesting this course of action. Your goal should be to teach the course material that you have been assigned — but there is nothing wrong with including some direct, well-chosen applications that apply to the material and appeal to you and the students. It is not "pandering" to the students to use the course materials and content in a meaningful way.

For a more advanced view of this topic, see a later section, The Perry Model.

Advice to International T.A.s

It can be very difficult to leave one's own culture and come to another, only to be asked to teach to "foreign" students, maybe in a "foreign" language.

Earlier, I mentioned briefly how a new graduate student has a wealth of first semester problems: setting up an apartment, finding a roommate, opening a checking account, finding a grocery store — and, all the while, trying to learn how to be a student and teacher. And, when you have just come from another country, these problems are compounded exponentially: how do you get a social security number so that you can receive a paycheck, what is an "I-9" anyway, do you have to carry a passport all the time, where do you find *ramen* noodles, how much money do you really need to live on in the States, etc.

I am very sympathetic with your problems — I lived through this same experience, not once, but twice — but here I will concentrate on the teaching aspects of your situation. First, I will address the question of how to get through the first few days in the classroom in the United States, and then I will talk briefly about the cultural aspects of teaching in another country.

A First T.A. Assignment — What to Do, How to Cope

First, it is all right to be nervous; I would be surprised if you weren't. All new T.A.s — at least, all the ones who care about the job and want to do well — are nervous. Just remember that, although you may not have taught before, at least in the United States, those who chose you to be a graduate student have recognized you as an intelligent human being. They did not select you for failure; instead, you have been recognized for your potential for success. One of the early measures of this potential is the number and quality of the questions you ask.

Some questions to consider about your T.A. assignment:

Can you spend the first semester or two grading in a more advanced class rather than having to stand in front of a group of freshman calculus students? If so, you will have an opportunity to take some English language classes and watch some (terrible) television to get the language down better. You can also have a couple of office hours to do some one-to-one tutoring to increase your language abilities.

Is it possible to get a class that is an "easy job," not necessarily in the sense of material simpler to understand, but in the sense of material "easier to explain to students?" By this I mean that students in Fourier series, for instance, have fewer misunderstandings than those in a supposedly trivial freshman algebra class; thus Fourier series, although harder to understand, can be easier to teach.

If a grading assignment or an easy job is not possible, there are still ways in which you can help yourself get through the semester with your sanity, and your dignity, intact.

Find yourself two "mentors" you think you can trust; one from your home country (if possible), and another from the United States. Ask them to advise you, in a semiformal way. Then, before your first class, after you have done the first homework assignment, have a mock class with (at least) the U.S. mentor. In this mock class, go to a board and do some problems as you would in the first day's class. Concentrate on pronunciation – especially of difficult words like "continuity" and "theorem" that will appear in a mathematical context — write a lot on the board, and ask for advice. See how well you understand the comments, questions and advice that the mentor is giving you.

Next, go to your countryperson and ask some questions about what you should expect the students to be like. This is information that your countryperson will understand, but the T.A. from the U.S., having lived and taught only in the States, will not. (I will have more to say about cultural questions later in this section.)

Then go to your first class. As part of your introduction, explain to the students that you are from another country and new to teaching. Tell them that, to help them and yourself, you will be trying to speak slowly, that you intend to write a lot on the board, and that you would appreciate it if the students would occasionally help correct your pronunciation. When someone asks you a question, if you simply do not understand it, ask the other students for help in rephrasing it. If a student says that a problem can be done another way, offer him or her the chalk and ask if he or she will show you "at the board." In this way, you can see the solution in writing, rather than trying to understand your student's "Noo Yawk" (i.e., New York) accent. If a student says, "I don't understand," ask where on the board is the step that isn't clear, and fill in missing details at that specific point. If the student's response is that "None of it is clear," try to do the problem a different way, or start it again, but this time add in all possible details. If nothing is making sense, try to get the mentor to observe one of your classes to see where the problem lies. And, if all else fails, start writing up solution sets for the students — but, don't do this from day one, because they will become a crutch for you, and the students will expect them all the time.

After the first or second week, you should not need to use your mentor to practice every class. However, he or she can still be useful for occasional discussions of how to approach individual topics, how to pronounce new words that come up, and how to deal with situations you have never experienced in your home country.

Some other suggestions as to how to treat the first few days of class can be found in other sections, for instance, in Day One.

Cultural Aspects of Teaching

Learning about the culture in which you are teaching is at least as important as knowing how to speak the language, yet this aspect of teaching is often overlooked.

When I moved to Canada, the first lecture I gave was on my research. Since I spoke English and they spoke an only slightly better English, I didn't feel that there would be any particular problem. At one point in the lecture, however, after some people asked me about details, I asked, brightly, "Any more objections?" The response, by a number of people, was "Oh! We weren't objecting!" Of course, I also hadn't thought that they were really "objecting"; I was just using a word I had used many times before to indicate the fact that I would be willing to answer more questions. Then, after a few more incidents of this sort in restaurants, banks and the like, I suddenly realized that, although I may be a reasonably polite "American," I'll never be a polite Canadian-American.

When you walk into a classroom, you carry with you many assumptions; for instance, what students are like, how they should address you, whether and how they should ask questions, and how they should dress and act, just to name a few. Many of these assumptions come from the way you were taught in your home country; you will be expecting similar treatment from your students here.

Sorry, but let me tell one more story from my past:

When I was in Japan, I had a chance to observe some college mathematics teaching. In each case, when the instructor walked into class, the students stood out of respect. After they sat back down, the instructor then delivered a lecture at the board from yellowed sheets of paper without any questions from the students, who spent their time quickly taking as many notes as they could. Then, when the instructor had finished his fifty-minute lecture, the students again rose as he quickly left.

My point in telling this story is not to claim that a particular method of instruction is better or worse than another (although I do express some opinions as to the efficacy of interactive methods elsewhere in these notes), but rather to show how different such methods can be.

In the States, most students will have come from high schools where they were encouraged to ask questions in class, sometimes merely by interrupting the teacher; and where they were often required to work in small groups in rather noisy classroom settings. Thus, if you have come from an atmosphere like the one I described seeing in Japan, you may be shocked by what you think is insolent behavior on the part of your American students. Occasionally I feel as if I should apologize for some of what I see in the U.S. classroom; at the same time, I can understand how our students can profit from being able to ask a question when they want to — within reason.

As usual, I have some suggestions.

If you find, as I do, that students should be able to ask questions, but in a more mannerly way than by just yelling out, "That's not right! The answer should be five," then I propose that you tell them on day one that "I am open to questions. But, please raise your hand, so that I know who is asking the question, and so that I can finish my thought before answering you." (For more suggestions as to how to make your classroom more active, look at such sections as The Active Classroom and Motivating Students.) If, on the other hand, you believe that students should hear what you have to say before they start asking questions, ask them to hold their questions until you have fully explained the topic, the example or the exercise you are working on. In short, remember that the culture may not be yours, but the classroom *is* yours, and it is your right to decide, *within reason*, what is the best way for you to get the material across.

A short list of thoughts about teaching and living in another culture:

- Although it is usually easier to live with, room with, and deal with people from your own country and culture, you will find yourself learning so much more if you make the effort to spend as much time as you can in the "native culture."

- There are a number of advantages to T.A.ing in the U.S. You will learn the language, and that can help you in your studies as well as in your teaching. Further, if you decide to stay in the States after graduation, you will need all the language skills you can get for your job.

- If you go back to your home country, your knowledge of English will also be helpful there in your job and your research.

- If you find that some classroom situations are bothering you, talk them over with your mentor from your own country. The problem may turn out to be easily solvable, or it may really reflect some cultural differences. In either case, you can get advice on dealing with the situation.

- You do not have to accept what you perceive to be improper behavior on the part of your class. If you find the students acting in a way you think is unacceptable, talk it over with your U.S. mentor. In this way, you can gain some valuable insight into how standards vary between your own culture and the one in the United States.

- And finally, enjoy your teaching experience. View it as an opportunity to learn about another culture. Try to develop a classroom atmosphere that is in keeping with your personality, while at the same time is relaxed. Why not have some fun while you are getting a degree?

Some Silly Stuff...

[This section recapitulates some of the material from the earlier Checklist section, but in a bit more detail.]

Everyone who starts a new job walks into a place that has a life of its own: you will encounter all sorts of "silly stuff" too small to consider, and at the same time too important not to consider. And, if you ignore all the little details below, a lot of people will get annoyed with you.

For instance, where are the bathrooms located in your new building? More importantly, what are the emergency procedures for the places where your classrooms are located?

If you cut your finger, can you get a bandage? If one of your students has a health problem during class, whom can you contact to get aid?

Where do you get keys to the buildings and offices? Do you have to pay a deposit for the keys? If you give extra classes or review sessions in the evenings, will you have to reserve classroom space? Don't assume that you can "just use the same room" on Tuesday night as you did on Friday afternoon.

Where do you get chalk and erasers for the boards? Carry an extra piece of chalk to the classroom. (I know an instructor who once used his shirt to erase the board; his students never forgot.)

Find out the methods and "rules" of using the copy machines. How many copies may be made for your class? Can you make personal copies for a fee? Wouldn't it be nice if you didn't have to bother the staff each time the machine runs out of paper?

Ask where and when you get your paycheck. When is the first payday? The last? Can you get direct deposit to your bank? Is there a possibility of additional pay in the summer?

Can you tutor for cash? Or is your institution opposed to that because they consider it a conflict of interest?

Learn how to search for and check out books at the library.

Find out whether your keys to the building work on evenings and weekends.

Who decides where your desk is located? Is there a lock on the door so that your books and sweater don't "disappear," or do you need to carry everything around with you all the time?

What are the rules about textbooks? Do they have to be returned at the end of the semester? Can you go ahead and write all your notes in the margins?

Where do you turn in grades at the end of the semester?

Are there syllabus files? Or files of old exams? Who can use them?

Do you have to pay for your own pencils and paper? How about transparency sheets if you use an overhead?

What do all the staff members do? How much of it "concerns you"?

What are the general rules about how much time you should be spending on your teaching? How many office hours are considered appropriate?

When students ask you advising questions you don't know the answer to, to whom should you send them?

Who is your immediate supervisor, and how often should you report to him or her, if at all? Will he or she be handing out a syllabus, or some old exams? Who will make up the homework assignments for the students?

Do you have to go to the calculus lecture you've been assigned to as recitation instructor?

What is expected of you at "vacation time?" Can you go home during study week, say, or during that part of exam week before your class takes its final? Or will the course overseer get angry because you aren't available for office hours and to help with the makeup of the exam?

Hey, there's lots of "silly stuff" you have to ask about! I'll bet you can think of ten questions I missed! And every school is different; don't assume that what you did when you T.A.ed as an undergraduate or when you were working on that master's degree will apply now.

...And Not So Silly Stuff

There is bound to come a time when you have a disagreement with your course leader. I can think of many ways in which this can come about; for now, I will discuss two hypothetical situations.

In the first case, you find that Professor Dimble, the lecturer in calculus this semester, seems to be having an inordinately difficult time explaining the text to the students. He is a former teaching award winner at your institution, Grand U., but his eyesight, hearing and — most importantly — his memory seem to be failing him. All of this is causing the students no small amount of consternation, and costing you and the other T.A.s a great deal of time. Students are coming to you for "additional lectures," bombarding you and the other T.A.s with lots of questions outside of class. When you demur over extra evening sessions, they respond, "But we *need* you — Professor Dimble just doesn't make sense!" Meanwhile, you are in the last full year of your schooling; you're writing your thesis, trying to finish up a paper for publication, and looking for a job. You don't need the added stress of teaching basic calculus to freshmen for a graduate student's salary.

So what do you do? Well, one possible solution would be to make your feelings known to all. Complain to the students, to your thesis advisor, to other T.A.s, to the chair, to the dean! You could also refuse to give the students extra help; "After all, I didn't create this problem." You could even call and tell your family. This would certainly get your position across; even Professor Dimble would probably find out, his hearing problems notwithstanding.

What will be the result of your complaints? Well, the students will know how you feel. But if you don't offer them some help they won't see you as part of the solution, just another obstacle in the way to their learning calculus.

Your thesis advisor will see you as a "young researcher" who doesn't understand the professional culture, who will mature eventually, maybe after you get to your "first real job." He or she won't say this to you directly, of course, but you'll hear about it later through the grapevine.

The other T.A.s will think that you're a prima donna, that you're more worried about your thesis and your career than about your fellow T.A.s or your students.

The chair will try to explain to you about Professor Dimble. "You have to understand, he's getting old. We know about the problem, and maybe by next year we can do something, but right now, we're in the middle of the term, and it would be really unfortunate to pull him out of class. But thanks for the information." [Yeah, sure!]

Meanwhile, the Dean's viewpoint will be "Why doesn't he keep this at the department level? That's what a chair is for."

And poor Professor Dimble; he'll feel saddened, surprised, shy, confused, improperly maligned. Personally insulted.

Well, "solution one" didn't work too well. Is there another?

Let's back up. What's wrong with giving the students a once a week "review session"? Perhaps you could trade off with two or three of the other T.A.s, so that you only have to conduct one of these sessions once or twice a month. Then if you quietly go to the chair (not the dean; keep it at the department level) to explain the situation, he or she will be grateful for your extra work and may even be able to "compensate you and your fellow T.A.s," if only with a reduced load in the next semester.

If your advisor asks why you aren't getting out that twelfth draft of your joint paper, you can quietly explain the details. He will then tell other members of the department, and more importantly, will write in his recommendation letter to other schools that you are "a mature young mathematician who willingly took on extra duties to solve a small [!?] teaching problem we had here at Grand U." This will make you sound like someone another school would be happy to have in the tenure-stream position it is advertising.

You will have preserved your good relations with your fellow T.A.s — except for that one person who refused to help you — and Professor Dimble will finish up his illustrious career with his honor intact.

Now to the second sticky situation: Having survived Professor Dimble, you are given what the chair considers "an easy assignment." Again, you will have a section of calculus, but this time it's with Professor Aggress. From the "git-go," the good professor is after students. "Are they all as dumb as they seem?" is the first question he asks you. He calls your homework grading into question; "You're too easy on them, and you didn't grade number fifteen properly" he tells you in front of a group of T.A.s and faculty in the department lounge. Then he insults other faculty in front of you, and you hear from your officemate that he is saying some unkind things about you to them. Further, Professor Aggress gives really difficult exams (the students say that they're "impossible"), and wants to have no curve. "As far as I'm concerned, if they can't get a '60' on this exam, they just shouldn't be taking mathematics."

OK, you survived Ole Dimble, so you should be professional enough by now to know that it will do no good to simply scream at Professor Aggress. After all, shouting and insulting are his stock in trade; he's been at it for the last thirty-six years. Well, you were professional with Dimble, let's try the same approach with Aggress.

First of all, ask yourself whether you really did grade number fifteen incorrectly. If so, apologize and offer to do it over. Then, when the next exam comes around, when you make up your grading key, ask Professor Aggress if you can show it to him to see if it "looks like what he wants."

When the students come to complain to you about Professor Aggress' attitude, do not talk badly about him. You and the entire department may completely agree with their complaints, but whatever you say will not change the situation one iota. Further, if it gets back to the professor, it will only end up causing you to be castigated by the chair or someone else in authority.

Instead, concentrate on making an effort to keep the exams and grading scheme as reasonable as possible. To help the students, look back at the first exam to see whether the problems were simply chosen from among the really hard ones, or whether they were totally out of line. If the former is the case, occasionally use class time to discuss with the students some of the later problems in each section. If it's the latter, *maybe*, after you've done your best to get into Professor Aggress' good graces, you might be able to suggest some possible problems for the later exams — ones that the students have some chance of working.

Remember, there's a huge difference between liking a person and working with that person. You do not have to sit in the coffee room and defend Professor Aggress' attitudes. In point of fact, the professor's insolence seems to be coming from some "deep-seated" problem that no one in the department is likely to be able to solve. But, that isn't your job — your goal is simply to be an honest, straightforward, professional person.

Of course, one of the ironies of this situation is that, if you really are professional, courteous, helpful to the students, and sensitive to Professor Aggress' attitudes, he may just ask to have you as a T.A. again the next semester. This is one of the difficulties you will have to guard against; on the other hand, you have done such a great job that I certainly don't need to tell you how to handle this problem. (Maybe you can just finish your thesis and graduate instead.)

Using Cognitive Models
to Make Appropriate Problems

[This section is a slight revision of a paper written by Mary Ann Malinchak Rishel and me.]

What makes examination questions easy or difficult? To some extent, it is the students' level of preparation and their attitude toward taking tests. These are internally applied forces coming from the test takers themselves. But there are also external stimuli at work here, such as the difficulty of the examinations we instructors construct.

Some years ago, a variety of individuals began to study what are now called **cognitive patterns** — the ways by which individuals learn information. By now, a number of books and articles have been written offering models of what are termed levels of cognition; i.e., the levels of difficulty of concepts, ideas, questions. Most of these texts are more applicable to the arts than to the sciences or mathematics (cf. Chaffee [7], Vygotsky [30]), but one that has been successfully used in mathematics is due to Benjamin Bloom [3].

The Bloom model splits cognition into six levels. From lowest to highest, these levels are:

Knowledge, comprehension, application, analysis, synthesis and **evaluation**.

Knowledge, Bloom's lowest category, pertains to whether the student has absorbed and can successfully reiterate the concept being taught. For example, in a first-semester calculus class we instructors might apply this principle to teaching the definition of the word "limit." To see whether the students have absorbed that definition, we can ask the logical but not particularly inspired question, "Can you define the word 'limit'?" This is an acceptable question; for the students to master the concept, they must be able to articulate it.

A note here before we go on: Bloom's use of the word "knowledge" in reference to the lowest level of cognition has sometimes been called into question. Many people have suggested that they believe the word "knowledge" indicates more cognitive awareness than Bloom seems to ascribe to it. Alternatives such as memorization and recitation have been suggested. The word **recall** might be used to indicate that the student is trying to reproduce what the faculty member has taught.

Let us now aim for higher levels of questions by going to the next level in Bloom's model.

A second level of cognition described by Bloom is **comprehension**. Do the students have some understanding higher than mere memorization of the concept under consideration? Here we mathematics instructors may ask, "When you think of the word 'limit,' what do you see and how does this relate to the standard definition?"

Once the students have shown ability at the level of comprehension, they can be asked an **application** question: "If you were trying to extend the definition of limit to three dimensions, how might you try?" With an assignment of this sort, we are attempting to get the first-semester calculus student to extend their intuition to third-semester concepts. Notice, of course, that since the topic of functions of two or more variables has not generally been introduced in the first-semester course, such a question is probably not a good one for an examination; it is, however, a reasonable discussion topic for a classroom situation.

An even higher level of cognitive thought that we might ask of a student is that of **analysis**. Here the student must take apart the concept in question and put it back into context while considering the implications. For example:

> Use words and pictures to investigate what happens to the function
> $$z = f(x,y) = xy/(x^2 + y^2)$$
> as x and y head toward zero along the two distinct paths $x = y$ and $x = 0$.

This will not be an easy question for first-semester students to answer; they will need help in finding the way because the reasoning requires an inductive leap. At this level of complexity, we might ask the student to write out the thinking in natural language as a way of articulating the mathematical concepts. This could be done at the board, as homework, as a class project or in an individual paper, depending on time constraints. Note, however, that for a third semester or higher calculus student, the above question might simply be one at Bloom's comprehension level.

Synthesis refers to the coalescing of analysis into an argumentative claim, a difficult and complex cognitive process for most students, but one that can guide them to a more sophisticated level of mathematics. Topics of this type can include hypothetical definitions, various historical treatments, or differing interpretative views. A typical synthesis topic: Discuss historical factors that led from Cauchy's definition of limit to Weierstrass's definition. Such topics best lend themselves to writing assignments.

Of course, a synthesis question can also be quite sophisticated, and we would be unlikely to suggest it to students in a first-semester calculus course. However, we might be interested in spending a few minutes discussing such a topic in class so as to give the students an understanding of how mathematics is not "written in stone," how it changes over time, how intuition solidifies into definition and theorem, and other related topics.

In a synthesis assignment, we can modify the expectations we hold for students. Claims can be low-level or high, depending on whether the thesis and subsequent "proof" reach back to the earlier levels of critical thought — those of application, comprehension and knowledge — or up to a high level like evaluation and argument. Generally, a synthesis paper includes most, if not all, cognitive categories; since the response will be complex, the student will address at least one high-level idea.

The highest level of comprehension in Bloom's model is called **evaluation**, where the student shows that she can embody the concept itself as well as all the cognitive levels described previously. At this cognitive level, we might ask for a major paper, since obviously these questions require a substantial effort from the student. For instance, we might ask: "Why is it so hard for people to absorb the epsilon-delta definition of limit?" An evaluation discussion is sometimes called an **argument**. Argument papers make for quality major projects, as in "Discuss how Newton's and Leibniz' views of calculus differed, and the implications of each person's approach for the history of thought and for the teaching of mathematics."

An Example from Infinite Series

This sample comes from Tom Rishel's classes.

To find out if students have been listening in lecture, Tom sometimes asks a quick quiz question at the recall level; for instance:

Find the limit of the series:
$$3/2 + 3/8 + 3/32 + 3/128 + \cdots$$

This simply asks the students to substitute the appropriate numbers into the formula for convergence of geometric series.

To gauge the students at the level of comprehension, he proposes that they:

Find $\lim[1 - 4 - 6 + \sum (3/2)(1/4)^n]$.

Here Tom is testing whether students know the above formula. Then he can find out whether they have absorbed the fact that, as he has said a number of times in class, adding or subtracting a finite number of terms to a series does not affect its convergence or divergence.

The following qualifies as an "analysis" question in a freshman class:

Find all a and r such that $\sum ar^n$ converges.

This last is a possibility for either a longer quiz question or an examination problem.

The next question, a "synthesis" problem, was used as a major part of a final exam:

Discuss the infinite series you have seen in this course. Include convergence tests, and provide examples of series for which each test does and does not work.

Although students did not exactly appreciate the above question, Tom found out a great deal about what they had learned about infinite series.

An "evaluation" project, much too involved to be considered a mere examination question, is one given in a mathematical exposition course:

> Trace the historical development of the concept of convergence. Include some analysis of Euler's work on defining the exponential, along with a discussion of the Riemann integral, Cauchy's "tests" versus Cauchy's "proofs," Weierstrass' work, and G.H. Hardy's contributions to series tests.

Levels of Cognition and Tutorials

Once we understand levels of cognition, we see that we have been using them in everyday situations:

A student walks into our office and says, "I can't factor $10x^2 - x - 3$." In Bloom's model, this is a knowledge question. We show her how to factor the polynomial, then suggest, "Now you try the next one, $15x^2 - x - 1$." We are testing comprehension.

Next, we wonder if she can find a way to factor a cubic. Here, we are asking for application, and also an analysis. The student now wants to know, "Is there a formula for finding the roots of all possible polynomials?" She's having us analyze and synthesize our knowledge of algebra.

Finally, when she blurts out, "Why do we need to know this? Can you give me a real world application? What's algebra good for, anyway?" she's leading toward evaluation; she wants a reasonable argument as to why she should learn the subject.

Of course, we have been dealing with such students all our academic lives. The point here is that when we understand the cognitive levels of the questions and answers we are dealing with, we will better understand the cognitive levels of the students. Then we can design our curriculum, questions and exams to fit those levels.

Course Design and Cognition

Although the content and methodologies of calculus and algebra courses are usually (though not always) quite well defined, the same is not necessarily true in other areas of mathematics, such as history of mathematics or geometry. Here, too, knowledge of cognitive levels aids in course construction and application.

Here is a description of a geometry course for students who "know no geometry" [26], constructed around the Bloom model:

Start by asking the students what geometric words they know or remember. At this point, they are working on the level of knowledge, offering words like point, line, plane; names like Euclid and Pythagoras; such concepts as theorem or axiom; vague terms like shape and solid. Spend some time asking the students to catalogue their randomly chosen terms into categories; what makes words like point or Pythagoras different from surface or theorem? This allows students to show how much they comprehend the terms of geometry, and to analyze differences and similarities in the concepts.

Now ask: "What is geometry?" This is a deep question, too deep for a real answer on the first day of class and one that requires a good deal of synthesis and evaluation. Allow students to find a definition that appeals to them and suggest that as a "working definition" of the concept. Then give them an assignment that challenges their definition.

For instance, students almost always describe geometry as "earth measurement." A good assignment that confronts this definition begins by having them measure the height of a large building — an application of their knowledge of geometry — only to find out by subsequent analysis of their methodologies that the technique they have used does not work on the surface of the earth. Then go on to the more sophisticated problems that occur because of the counterexamples that can be constructed; questions like: "What do triangles look like on the surface of the earth?" Such questions are very analytic and give the students a feel for how the rules of mathematics are constructed.

The course is now opened out upon a plethora of analytic questions that lend themselves to writing and discussion:

"What is an analogue to a 'straight' line on the surface of the earth?"
"How would you measure angles on the earth?"
"What is the difference between the surface of the earth and the earth itself?"

Further, you can address synthetic and evaluative questions:

"How many surfaces are there? And what does the word 'surface' mean?" "If Euclid knew the earth was round, why did he say he was studying geometry? What was his definition of geometry, and how might it differ from ours?" "What are 'straight lines' in space? Can we even talk about them when there is no 'grid' to compare them with? And if we cannot talk about straightness in space, how do we know how to get to the moon?"

None of these questions is obvious, yet all come out of only a few hours of simple discussion and seemingly trivial writing assignments given to moderately skeptical students who are supposedly not at all mathematically inclined.

Some Final Considerations

Although we have chosen Bloom's vertical model of cognition, there are others that are also useful in the processes described in this paper. For instance, see Chaffee [7], who offers a horizontal model based more on student writing strategies. Another model, more linguistic in format, is offered by Vygotsky [30]. See also Piaget [24] for a discussion of cognitive strategies in young learners.

Another simple cognitive model from composition courses, somewhat overlapping with Bloom's, consists of just three classifications of writing: **personal, informational** and **argumentative.** One personal paper might be "I chose to do mathematics because I found it as creative as art"; another is "My mind is more inclined to algebra than geometry."

Most mathematical papers fall into the informational category: "The large-scale geometry of the universe can be partially explained by curvature in two and three dimensions"; or "Messages can be sent with (almost) complete security." Thesis statements formed around business applications of linear programming and fractals and fractal dimensions can also fall into this category.

Argument papers, as much rhetorical as mathematical, have either soft or hard theses. A soft thesis requires only information to prove its claim through a lower level of cognition; a hard thesis, unless it employs sophisticated statistics, must be supported by more analysis and interpretation. Examples of soft theses might be the following: "Euclidean geometry does not fully explore the world around us," or "Writing assignments provide an effective form of evaluation in the mathematics classroom." Some examples of hard theses, depending on how they are approached, are: "Statistical analysis shows that cancer rates highly correlate with cigarette smoking," and "Better socialization in middle school leads to higher retention rates of women in mathematics and science programs."

By using cognitive models as guides in our mathematical teaching in ways that our writing colleagues have long done in composition, we can move students to deeper levels of understanding of mathematics. In the classroom, where students often ask, "What's it good for," the use of cognitive techniques can help them, and us, find answers to this kind of question.

The Perry Model

William Perry [23] published a theory of student development that has been very influential in higher education. The basic model has been modified in various ways; Belenky, *et al* [2] have revised it to fit gender differences, and Culver and Hackos [10] have done the same for the engineering disciplines.

Perry's original model consists of nine stages of development. I will describe a simplified (some might say oversimplified) four-stage model and briefly discuss possible implications for mathematics.

The four stages of student development are:

1. Basic duality,
2. Multiplicity,
3. Relativism,
4. Commitment.

In **basic duality**, the world is split in two; the only possibilities are right or wrong. In this mode, students see their instructors as authority figures who have all the answers. Instructors who do not instill "the correct answers," who want to explore all the alternatives, are merely bad teachers who are playing tricks on the students.

Multiplicity is the next stage of development in Perry's model. (In his original study, Perry splits this process into three stages.) In the main, "multiplicity" means here that the student now believes that "it's all a game." At first, the students are sure that there is still a right answer and that the instructor is just making them play along until the correct response is found. Later in the multiplicity phase, the students may decide that the instructor doesn't know the answer either; "He can't be any good as a teacher because he doesn't even know what we know." Later yet, the students may decide to believe that "anyone may have his or her own opinion."

From this stage, students then jump to the position of **relativism**, where "anything goes — all positions are equally valid. No one can argue against my outlandish position (however badly reasoned), because there is no absolute right or wrong."

In the final stage, **commitment**, students take into account positive and negative aspects of decisions they are considering, and then make balanced judgements as to what path to follow. In Perry's nine-stage model, he splits this process into parts that depend on the depth of the commitment.

The implications of the Perry model for mathematics and its teaching are important. I will discuss just one.

Students who are in the basic duality and multiplicity phases of growth sometimes say that they like mathematics "because in math all the answers are known." When they are challenged on some point in a sociology or English class, they often use mathematics and science as models of "correct" worldviews. Later, when these students find out that "ambiguous assumptions" are also made in theorems, they can become disillusioned with mathematics itself or the way it's being taught. Thus, their subsequent problems with ability to prove theorems can often be traced to their view of education itself, and not simply in their refusal to get the "theorem-proof" concept. One possible implication of this last conclusion, if true, may be that courses in proof theory for sophomores must be constructed to take into account the question of students' belief structures.

But I may be delving too far into a theory of learning for a text at this level. The implications of the Perry model are intriguing, however, and you may wish to pursue them further.

Finding Voice Through Writing in Mathematics

I am going to describe one telling example of a classroom situation from the school year just ended, after which I will make some gross generalizations from this sample of size one. The generalizations I make, however, will have come from over a dozen years of using expository methodologies in much of my teaching. Further, this single example is rather characteristic of what I have seen from my students.

I teach a course in geometry for people who "know no geometry" — whatever that means — and I get a rare and wonderful mix of students from all the various schools at Cornell University.

Last fall, one of my Arts College students, whom I shall call "Allison," came to class for the first three weeks or so, then didn't show up for another three weeks. One late afternoon she reappeared at my office door. "I tried to quit your class," she told me, "but my dean [one of the undergraduate advising deans] told me I had to come back." Then Allison said what she might have thought was a compliment; "The dean said if I couldn't finish your class, I couldn't finish any math class. So I guess I need to catch up on my old assignments."

We do a variety of topics in my class, some easy, some hard, some "funky" — like the ones I described in the Using Cognitive Models section earlier in the text.

I end the course with a final project. Students write a "longish" paper on a subject we commonly choose: I have individual conferences with each of the students. They and I jointly decide on a geometrically related topic of interest about which they will do some research. Then they present a short talk to the class on the subject, after which they write up the results.

Allison, who had not previously shown much interest in any individual topic of the course, told me that she was very intrigued by the discussion we had in class about nonorientable surfaces. She said she didn't really understand these surfaces, stating, "I'd like to try to do something with them, but I don't know what." Now, you have to understand that this topic is one of the truly difficult ones in the course, if only because nonorientable surfaces don't "really exist" in three-dimensional space. I tried to talk some sense into Allison; "OK," I replied, "you can research that for the next few days, and then if it seems too hard, you might try something like the golden ratio, say." In other words, "Here's an easy topic for when you come to your senses."

Allison was beginning her search for **voice**.

Three days later, Allison was back. "I still like the nonorientable surface topic, but it's really hard — what can I try?" I asked her again if she wouldn't really rather work on the golden ratio, and she said, "…no, not nearly as interesting." So I mentioned that we got into the topic of surface through looking at the Euler characteristic of the torus and other surfaces that can be constructed from the torus. I suggested that she might try to do the same for the most basic nonorientable surface, called the projective plane, and the other surfaces that can be constructed from it. "And if that doesn't work," I said brightly, "we still have plenty of time to study the golden ratio."

Two days later, Allison was back. "I tried some of the Euler stuff, but it's really hard." "OK," I replied, "let's break it into small pieces; we'll figure out how we found the Euler characteristic of the torus." We sat down, and with our notes from earlier classes we reconstructed the proof that the Euler characteristic of the torus is the number zero. (You don't have to understand this type of mathematics to get the meaning of this point; in fact, you may better appreciate the pedagogy if you don't "get" all the mathematics.) "Now," I told Allison, "you go home and try the same for the projective plane." ("Then we can get on to the golden ratio," I thought, but didn't say.)

During our dialogue, Allison used voice as reflection, as a way to reach the next more difficult level of thought.

Two days later, Allison had found the Euler characteristic of the projective plane. "But that's not enough; now what?" "Well, now you can find the characteristic of connected sums of two projective planes. Look in your notes for our proof for the torus case and see how you can change it." A few days later, after Allison showed me her proof, she moved on to finding a formula for connected sums of many projective planes, thus showing that she had taught herself to work inductively.

Allison was now ready to give her talk; on the next two pages is her handout from her talk to the class.

If I were to finish at this point, you might congratulate me for being able to help a student discover some rather deep mathematics by getting her to split a huge problem into several small ones. And that is not such a bad lesson for an instructor of mathematics — or any other subject — to learn. But actually, this is where my learning from Allison really begins.

The next day, Allison was back to my office, almost in tears. "But I don't have a paper!" "What do you mean, you don't have a paper?" "I mean it's good stuff and all, but it's not a *real paper* — it's just a bunch of formulas. Do you know what I mean? I mean, I still need to write my real paper for the final project!" In other words, Allison wanted more. She wanted a narrative! Oh, sure, she had done hard work, but she didn't have her story, her "real research." I was flabbergasted; how could she diminish such a solid mathematical text? After thinking for awhile, I was finally able to make the suggestions you see in the margins of Figure 2.

Math 150

RP2

Step 1: The Euler Characteristic of RP2
  A) Triangulate
  B) Count Vertices   V = 2 + 3 = 5

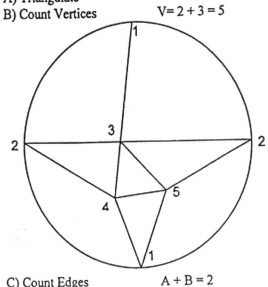

  C) Count Edges   A + B = 2
                           C through L = 10
                           E = 2 + 10 = 12

  D) Count Faces   I through VIII = 8
                           F = 8

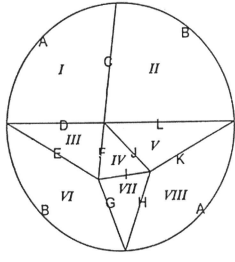

                           The Euler Characteristic of RP2 =
                                 V - E + F
                                 5 - 12 + 8 = 1
                                    so, x (RP2) = 1

Figure 1

Step 2: The sum of n RP2's

For every RP2 you add on (RP2 # RP2) you must subtract 2 (-2)
(My informal reason. if you stick two things together, you lose two faces, so you must subtract two)
We know x (RP2) = 1 , so...
x (RP2 # RP2) = x (RP2) + x (RP2) - 2 (faces)
$$1 \ + \ \ 1 \ \ -2 = 0$$
Keep adding RP2's :
x (RP2 # RP2 # RP2) = x (RP2 # RP2) + x (RP2) - 2
$$0 \ \ \ + \ \ \ 1 \ \ -2 = -1$$

x (RP2 # RP2 # RP2 # RP2) = x (RP2 # RP2 # RP2) + x (RP2) - 2
$$-1 \ \ \ + \ \ \ 1 - 2 = -2$$

x (RP2 # RP2 # RP2 # RP2 # RP2) =
x (RP2 # RP2 # RP2 # RP2) + x (RP2) - 2
$$-2 \ \ \ + \ \ \ 1 - 2 = -3$$

We can then find a formula for n RP2's added together:

n	sum
1	1
2	0
3	-1
4	-2
5	-3

Rule:
$$x \text{ (RP2 # RP2 # } \ldots \text{ # RP2)} = -n + 2$$
$$x \ (n) = 2 - n$$

Side Note:

As mentioned earlier, 2 RP2's added together
x ($\underbrace{\text{RP2 # RP2}}_{K}$) = x (RP2) + x (RP2) - 2 (faces)
$$1 + \ 1 \ \ -2 = 0 \quad \text{so, } x \ (K^2) = 0$$
This is what we studied earlier as the Klein Bottle.
Here's another way to make a Klein Bottle, but a squared-off version:

Page 72. The pattern is shown in Fig. 5 and is best laid out on heavy square-ruled paper, with about an inch and a half to a unit. The solid lines are cut, and the dotted lines folded. The frequent half units are due to this pattern being made symmetrical, except for unit number 14 and its opposite number, *x*. The perspective views identify the numbered and lettered units, thus giving a guide for the folding after the cuts are made. Joints are butt, not overlap, so cellulose tape is used.

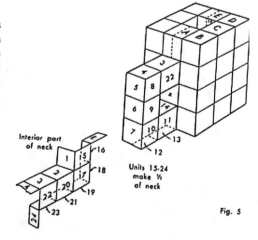

Interior part of neck

Units 15-24 make ½ of neck

Fig. 5

Figure 1 (*cont.*)

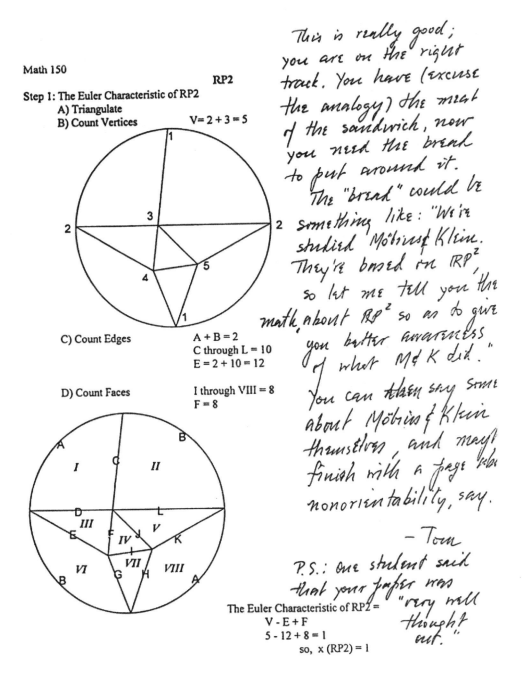

Math 150

RP2

Step 1: The Euler Characteristic of RP2
  A) Triangulate
  B) Count Vertices $V = 2 + 3 = 5$

  C) Count Edges $A + B = 2$
                          C through $L = 10$
                          $E = 2 + 10 = 12$

  D) Count Faces I through $VIII = 8$
                          $F = 8$

The Euler Characteristic of RP2 =
$$V - E + F$$
$$5 - 12 + 8 = 1$$
$$so, \ x(RP2) = 1$$

This is really good; you are on the right track. You have (excuse the analogy) the meat of the sandwich, now you need the bread to put around it. The "bread" could be something like: "We've studied Möbius & Klein. They're based on RP^2, so let me tell you the math about RP^2 so as to give you better awareness of what M & K did." You can then say some about Möbius & Klein themselves, and may finish with a page about nonorientability, say.

— Tom

P.S.: One student said that your paper was "very well thought out."

Figure 2 (*continued on the next page*)

Step 2: The sum of n RP2's

For every RP2 you add on (RP2 # RP2), you must subtract 2 (-2)
(My informal reason: if you stick two things together, you lose two faces,
so you must subtract two.)
We know x (RP2) = 1 , so...

x (RP2 # RP2) = x (RP2) + x (RP2) - 2 (faces)
$$1 + 1 \quad -2 = 0$$

Keep adding RP2's :

x (RP2 # RP2 # RP2) = x (RP2 # RP2) + x (RP2) - 2
$$0 \quad + \quad 1 \quad -2 = -1$$

x (RP2 # RP2 # RP2 # RP2) = x (RP2 # RP2 # RP2) + x (RP2) - 2
$$-1 \quad + \quad 1 - 2 = -2$$

x (RP2 # RP2 # RP2 # RP2 # RP2) =
x (RP2 # RP2 # RP2 # RP2) + x (RP2) - 2
$$-2 \quad + \quad 1 - 2 = -3$$

We can then find a formula for n RP2's added together:

n	sum
1	1
2	0
3	-1
4	-2
5	-3

Rule:

x (RP2 # RP2 # ... # RP2) = $-n + 2$
$$x (n) = 2 - n$$

Side Note:
As mentioned earlier, 2 RP2's added together
x (RP2 # RP2) = x (RP2) + x (RP2) - 2 (faces)
$$\underset{K}{\underbrace{}} \qquad 1 + 1 \quad -2 = 0 \quad \text{so, } x (K^2) = 0$$
This is what we studied earlier as the Klein Bottle.
Here's another way to make a Klein Bottle, but a squared-off version:

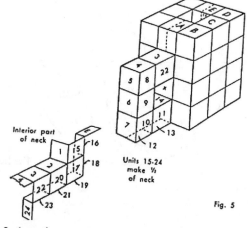

Page 72. The pattern is shown in Fig. 5 and is best laid out on heavy square-ruled paper, with about an inch and a half to a unit. The solid lines are cut, and the dotted lines folded. The frequent half units are due to this pattern being made symmetrical, except for unit number 14 and its opposite number, x. The perspective views identify the numbered and lettered units, thus giving a guide for the folding after the cuts are made. Joints are butt, not overlap, so cellulose tape is used.

Interior part of neck

Units 15-24 make ½ of neck

Fig. 5

Figure 2 *(cont.)*

Let me now show you (Figure 3) what Allison came up with as her "real paper," the one that wasn't just "a bunch of formulas." And as she moves through each version, she gains more confidence in articulating voice.

December 1998
Math 150

Projective Plane Geometry

I decided to do my final paper on RP2 because it was something I didn't understand. We had studied the Mobius strip and the Klein bottle in class, which are both based on RP2. So I went ahead and found out some more math about RP2 to help myself understand the concept better. In this paper I will discuss the math behind RP2 to give a better awareness of what Mobius and Klein did.

The Projective Plane, which is abbreviated as RP2, is obtained by "identifying antipodal points on the boundary of a disk." Its surface has a Euler characteristic = 1. Leonard Euler, for whom the Euler characteristic is named, was a Swiss Mathematician who lived in the eighteenth century. He discovered that "for any polyhedron that can be mapped on to the surface of a sphere (a 0-torus), the number of vertices plus the number of faces minus the number of edges always equals two." Several decades later, Simon Antoine-Jean Lhuilhier determined that this is not true for solids that have holes in them. For example, "on a 1-torus, vertices plus faces minus edges equals zero" . This general formula for a torus is: vertices + faces - edges = 2 - 2 X holes. The quantity (vertices + faces - edges) is called the *Euler number* of the solid.

RP2's surface has a Euler characteristic = 1. To prove this, you must first triangulate the surface, and then count vertices (V= 2 + 3 = 5), as shown below:

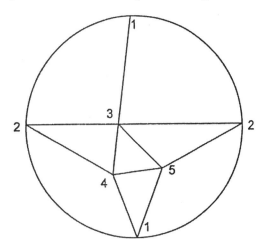

Figure 3 (*continued on the next 3 pages*)

Then you'd count the number of Edges (A + B = 2 , C through L = 10, so E = 2 + 10 = 12) and finally you'd count the number of Faces (I through VIII = 8, so F=8), as shown in the picture below:

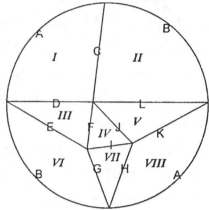

Therefore, the Euler Characteristic of RP2, according to Lhuilhier's formula (V - E + F), is equal to: 5 - 12 + 8 = 1.

To find the sum of *n* RP2's is another formula: X (RP2 # RP2 # . . .# RP2) = -*n* + 2 (or x (*n*) = 2 - *n*). I figured this out through a number of steps. First of all, for every RP2 you add on (RP2 # RP2), you must subtract 2 (-2). This is because if you stick two things together, you would lose two faces, so then you must subtract two from the overall sum. No matter what the object- a torus a Klein Bottle or RP2- when literally "sticking" two things together, you must lose two faces in order for them to "stick". Now, we know the Euler Characteristic of RP2 is equal to one [x (RP2) = 1], so adding two RP2's together would give us the following:

x (RP2 # RP2) = x (RP2) + x (RP2) - 2 (the faces we must subtract when
         1   +   1   - 2 = 0   adding)

Now we know that the Euler Characteristic of 2 RP2's is equal to zero. If we want to find the Euler Characteristic of three RP2's we'd do the same thing:

x (RP2 # RP2 # RP2) = x (RP2 # RP2) + x (RP2) - 2
         0   +   1   - 2   = -1

And we can keep doing this with four RP2's, and then five RP2's. If we did we'd get a table that would look like this:

n	sum
1	1
2	0
3	-1
4	-2
5	-3

Using a little previous math knowledge, I found the rule I mentioned earlier:

$$X (RP2 \# RP2 \# . . .\# RP2) = -n + 2$$
$$x (n) = 2 - n$$

This is the rule to find the sum of an infinite amount of RP2's added together.

Figure 3 *(cont.)*

RP2 is a nonorientable surface. A nonorientable surface is a surface "on which there exists a closed path such that the directrix is reversed when moved around this path." Fortunately I found a much more understandable description of orientability:

"Suppose that [a piece of] paper were infinitely thin. It has an upper side, consisting of an infinite set of points. On the underside is a corresponding set of points- but since the thickness equals zero they coincide with the upper set: *they are the upper set.* Yet we speak of 2 "sides." If they have no size, how can they have sides? How can they be orientated-right to left or front to back? Individually they cannot: but in a group they can be- for they are in a particular order, which is reversed when counted, or looked at from the other *side* or direction. This is an example of a line- a 1-dimensional space. We could make [spiral shaped holes all around a Mobius strip]. If we try this.. . all goes well for a while- then we find we are next to a hole we made before, and it is counterclockwise, because it was made from the opposite side, or direction. This means that the Mobius strip is what is called *nonorientable.* From this we can see that any 2-sided surface is orientable; any 1-sided surface is not."

Mobius was actually a German astronomer born on November 17, 1790 in Schulpforta, Saxony. He was a student at Leipzig University, and after graduating was appointed to Extraordinary Professor of Astronomy. Throughout his life he published a lot of his writing, such as *The Barycentric Calculus* and *Celestial Mechanics.* He was made Full Professor in Astronomy, then eventually appointed Director of the Observatory. It wasn't until 1858 that he discovered the complexities of the Mobius band (a strip of paper with a half twist joined at the ends- a lot more complicated than that seems), and ten years later he died. Some interesting things I found out about the Mobius band: If you cut the Mobius band lengthwise down the middle, when finished you'll find you can pull the band apart into one big loop. If you cut the Mobius band in thirds lengthwise, when finished you will end up with two interlinked loops. An interesting quote about the Mobius band: "The cultural pervasiveness of the notion of Mobius' band is now assured because, rather like some other popular mathematical metaphors, it has begun to be used in all kinds of contexts for which it is thoroughly inappropriate."

Two RP2's added together make up what is known as a Klein Bottle, which is another unorientable surface. "If one moves around on a Klein Bottle, one's right and life sides get interchanged as you move around, showing that it is a nonorientable surface". It can be constructed by glueing together the two ends of a cylindrical tube with a twist. Unfortunately this can't be done in 3-d space- it would have to intersect itself at some point. The picture would look something like this:

Figure 3 (*cont.*)

It isn't a true picture of the Klein Bottle, since it wouldn't actually be intersecting itself. The Klein bottle can only truly exist in 4-dimensional space: "one lifts up the narrow part of the tube in the direction of the 4th coordinate axis just as it is about to pass through the thick part of the tube, then drops it back down into 3-dimensional space inside the thick part of the tube."

Felix Klein, after whom the Klein Bottle was named, and an early Non-Euclidean Mathematician, was born April 25, 1849 in Dusseldorf, Prussia. He is best known "for his work on the connections between geometry and group theory, for results in function theory, and for his work in non-Euclidean geometry". Interestingly, he started out on his career with the intentions of becoming a physicist, but turned out making major discoveries regarding geometry. He published two papers *On the So-Called Non-Euclidean Geometry*, where he argued that "non-Euclidean geometry was consistent if and only if Euclidean geometry was consistent." At the time non-Euclidean geometry had been a controversial topic, and now its status had been raised because of Klein's work.

Topology is the study of shapes. More precisely, "it is the study of the properties that don't change when the shapes are twisted or stretched." In topology what matters are the numbers of holes and twists- for example a donut is a torus, but so is a mug. Topology involves many shapes, such as the Mobius Band, the Klein Bottle and the Projective Plane. I have learned a lot from my study of these surfaces and the people that discovered them. At the beginning of this class I had trouble understanding all of this- Non-Euclidean geometry seemed beyond belief. But now I can see just a little more clearly where exactly Mobius, Euler, and Klein's ideas were coming from.

Figure 3 (*cont.*)

Now, dear reader, we come to the moral of our story: Writing, speaking and homework problems are not an end in themselves, but rather a means to an end. And the end is to have students, and ourselves, understand that mathematics is one of the activities of the human mind — an activity that has a story. By this I mean that the subject has:

- A set of questions to be raised.
- Interesting examples drawn from the real world.

- Mental constructs that, whether or not they come from "reality," certainly do come from our minds.
- Reasoned, careful arguments aimed at describing, explaining and proving the works of those mathematical minds.
- Descriptions of the history and personalities involved.

All the above are highly approachable by students and faculty alike. In fact, one of the problems of much of the pedagogy of mathematics is that it does not leave us – students or faculty — with a clear, coherent narrative. Rather, too often we have an inordinately large set of disconnected "facts" to memorize.

In short, I believe that what Allison was telling me was that she wanted to work at the highest levels of human reasoning — and she needed narrative to do that. And, to create the narrative she had to give voice to her mathematics. She used voice and narrative to express extremely abstract concepts. And in doing so, she taught me how important voice and narrative are in the learning of mathematical skills.

Professional Questions

Letters of Recommendation

The first time a student asks you for a letter of recommendation, you will probably be surprised. As the surprise wears off, you will experience a sinking realization that you have no idea what to write.

If you really don't know the student, or if you cannot write a generally positive recommendation, you may suggest that he or she "might want to find someone who knows you better and can write a more specific letter." Of course you don't say, "I really don't think you're that good a student for the position you've applied for."

On the other hand, if you do remember the student and can write a positive letter about his or her potential, by all means do so. Here's how:

First, write as well and as carefully as you can; after all, you are being asked for a professional assessment. To help yourself and the candidate, find out what position he or she is applying for, and what the reason is for the letter. Is it for a summer job, maybe? Or is the student transferring to another institution, or maybe applying to a graduate or professional school or for a scholarship? Each possibility suggests the qualities the applicant will be asked to show, and will thus affect the letter you write. Ask for a resume, and ask the student his or her reason for interest in the position. A description of the job can also be helpful; get one from the student if you can.

Start your letter with: "[Student] has asked me for a letter of recommendation for [your job]."

Then: "I have known [student] since [date] in [capacity]."

Next: "My specific comments as to what I saw...." Here you can address such issues as "often came to class," "asked good questions," "got good grades," "worked well with others," and the like.

Now address the qualities described in the job description as being desirable: "motivated," "self-starter," "team player," etc. If you don't know what qualities the school or company is looking for, try to intuit what the future employer would want.

Finish with a comment as to the student's potential. If the student has indicated a reason for applying that seems to fit the qualifications of the job particularly well, say so. "Your request for candidates with some familiarity with the rigors of veterinary medicine fits well with Joan's background; she has spent a good deal of time volunteering at the local SPCA...."

Keep a copy of the letter, by the way. The student may well be back with another application in hand. And, the employer may call you for a follow up comment. "Did you really mean what you wrote?"

Jobs, Jobs, Jobs

Maybe you haven't heard, but there aren't any tenured T.A.s. Thus today is a good day to start looking for a job.

Go to a word processor. Put together a resume. Of course, your name, address and all the standard categories are on it. If you are a new T.A., you will probably have lots of white space where your **teaching**, **research** and **professional activities** should be. This white space is what you need to fill up over the next few years — if you are an older T.A., you should have done so already.

So, under **teaching**, you should try to get as varied a background as possible. Don't always T.A. in the engineering calculus section, even if you like that best. How is it you know you won't like the business students instead?

Ask to teach your own section of some course, then put together a small portfolio with a couple of your lesson plans and all the quizzes and exams. Put copies of your good course evaluations (they are good, right?) in that portfolio, along with any nice e-mails or letters from students.

Grade an advanced course in your area rather than teaching all the time. Ask to give a lecture or two in the course, then put that on your resume.

Write a teaching statement to put into your portfolio. You will need such a statement later on when you go up for tenure, so now is a good time to start to hone one.

In the **research** category, once you have reached the third year, you will probably have picked out a specialty. You can then write a short description of your topic for the resume. At the same time, you should write a couple of pages for the portfolio on the recent history of your topic, what the important theorems are, who is working in the area, and where your thesis topic sits relative to the work of others in the field.

If you are in your first or second year and haven't done any pure research yet, maybe you can describe an REU paper you wrote or your undergraduate thesis at your previous school.

In terms of **professional activities**, you can list any talks you have given. If you have never given talks, now is the time to start planning to do so. You have the possibility, from your first year in graduate school, to speak to the Math Club or the graduate student seminar. You can also call up your former professors at your undergraduate college and ask them if they'd like you to speak at their seminar the next time you're in town.

You should also join the American Mathematical Society and the Mathematical Association of America. Doing so shows that you have a real, professional interest in mathematics, both as a research area and in its teaching aspects.

Another professional activity that is more important than you may think at first is to go to MAA and AMS sectional and regional meetings. These are usually within a couple hundred miles of your home institution, and they give you a decent idea of the current teaching issues and hot research topics.

For more advice, check out the employment section of the AMS web page at www.ams.org. There's an especially good article there called *The Academic Job Search in Mathematics* — you'll see why I'm fond of it when you get there. The MAA web site also has some job information.

Mathematical Talks

Generally, you will be asked for one of two types of mathematical talks during your time as a graduate student: the "long talk," — of about an hour — and the "short one," about ten to twenty minutes. The long talk also splits into two: research-related, and expository.

Believe it or not, of the three types, I contend that the research-related one is the easiest to give. This is mainly because, first of all, you wouldn't be offered, nor would you accept, an invitation to speak about your research unless you were actively doing some. Further, now that you are actually doing research, you are somewhat of an expert at the topic. Thus, describing the history, stating the main theorems, discussing a couple of relevant examples, stating and "heuristically proving" your and others' results, and listing some open problems should all be no problem for you. The hardest part of such a talk is making sure you keep it interesting for the listener: What makes the problem significant? How can you make the audience care? What kinds of examples will give us a feeling that we understand the broad outline of the topic? What other examples or results will indicate the depth or power of the problem?

Putting such a research talk together is useful for you because it will offer you insight into your own work. Further, you will need to have such a talk for when you go onto the job market, so now is the best time to start preparing it.

A good expository talk is also not really hard to put together; it just takes time. What is a good topic for undergraduates that isn't usually covered in the traditional curriculum? Squaring the circle, say? Nonstandard analysis? Nonorientable surfaces? Cryptography? How about "Three new uses for matrices"? Or, "The statistics of baseball"? All these, and more, have been discussed in books and papers that you can refer to, and build from. These make good talks for sectional meetings of the MAA, or to graduate student seminars and colloquia, or to students at the colleges at which you are interviewing for a job.

As with the research talk, the expository talk should be coherent and interesting. Here, however, you should emphasize the history, examples and open questions of the topic, rather than precise definitions, proofs and other "dirty details" — not that these aren't important, but the interested listener can look them up later.

The short talk, which I will call "the ten-minute talk," is to me the most difficult, even though most neophytes think it is the easiest. The reason it is difficult is clear when you think about it: there is very little time in which to say anything important or useful. Many people reason, "Since they aren't giving me any time to say anything meaningful, I'll just 'wing it.'" This is a big mistake; most young mathematicians end up having to give short talks, and the worth of their work is gauged by the quality of their presentation. (My first talk was on the last day of a national meeting. I had an audience of three: the previous speaker, the next speaker, and A.H. Stone. Stone took notes on my talk.)

So how do you give a quality ten-minute talk? Start by "thinking backwards": What's the most important point you need to make? Make sure that point comes in the talk somewhere toward the end. Often you will think, "It's that new theorem of mine that's the really exciting thing," but are you sure of that? So often, the audience thinks that it's corollaries or examples that come from the theorem that are important, or maybe the questions that get answered or don't get answered that are really the reason for the talk.

When you know where your talk is heading, what do you need to get there? Is there a definition you need for comprehension? Then put it in. Similarly, an illustrative example will usually give the audience more sense of the topic than proofs. Also, make sure you indicate why the topic is important; whose theorem are you extending? What question are you answering? And what new problems have you uncovered? What are you going to try to prove next, and do you want to tell the audience this? (After all, you may want more time to construct your own proof.)

Of course, in ten minutes you won't be able to give proofs — at most, you'll have time for a statement or two of intuition — and then, usually only in response to a question from the audience.

So your talk starts, "In 1987, Jones proved...but he left open the question of.... I have a partial result in the hemi-demi-semi-typological case. First, I will define.... A simple example is.... Here's the main theorem.... It is proved through the use of Smith's theorem on.... An example of a space where the theorem works is.... and let me finish with a conjecture and some comments."

Now you have a talk, and you think it will be ten minutes long. Try it out on your officemate, and don't be surprised when it comes in at eighteen minutes and you feel pressured all through the practice session.

You can save some time by putting as much information as possible on transparencies; this should be worth about three to five minutes. Then there's the second example that you thought was so good, but your officemate found redundant; drop it. The fact that it could give the audience some new insight is a point you can use if there's a question period, or perhaps when someone stops you in the hallway two hours later to tell you how much they liked the talk.

Now you're down to twelve minutes. You can drop a definition that your officemate didn't know but everyone in your area of mathematics does. When you also remove two of the three "intuitive comments" you were going to put in at the end, you think you have nine minutes. So you try the talk on your officemate one more time, and sure enough, it is just under the ten-minute mark, although you still wish you could have put in one more of those last intuitive comments. At this point, you must understand that it's OK to feel that you could give the audience more; that intuitive comment could also come up in the question period, if people are interested. And if they aren't interested (sometimes audiences just aren't), well then, one more comment will just make them that much less excited.

What else? Well, in general, to repeat, put as much as possible on transparencies. This will save time, and it'll keep you from forgetting to say something important. Another general point: try not to appear rushed. If you need to talk fast to "get it all in," well, OK, but if that makes you look worried, people will have less confidence in your work.

Enjoy the experience as much as you can; after all, you know as much about the topic as anyone in the room, except, maybe, your advisor and one other person. And, those are the people you can learn from about where you should be going next — that's really why you came to speak, yes?

University and College Governance

I was talking to a full professor a few days ago when suddenly he asked, "What does a provost do, anyway?" I hope I don't insult this person by saying that I am surprised that people can spend upwards of thirty years in colleges and universities and still not know very much about how governance works.

Of course, every school has a different way of administration. For instance, colleges, which usually concentrate on undergraduate education, are not governed in the same way as universities, which have graduate schools and thus graduate deans. I will describe one model, but there are many others. You can use mine as a template for comparison.

Many people make the mistake of thinking that governance starts with the president of the university. It does not. For example, read the back of the ballot for trustees of Cornell University: "The University Bylaws vest supreme control over the University and all its divisions to the Board of Trustees." The board then delegates its responsibilities through a central administration and committee structure. At the top of the central administration sits a chief administrative officer, usually called the "president," who is responsible for academic quality, fundraising, public relations, financial management and institutional integrity. And, often, the success of the athletic program. Vice-presidents, for research, for finance, etc., are then subordinate to the president.

Most universities also have a chief academic officer, called a provost, who oversees the day-to-day workings of the various colleges within the university; e.g., the arts college, the engineering school, the business school, and the like. Some institutions have separate provosts for medical and business schools. Again, provosts tend to have a number of vice-provosts whose responsibilities are spelled out in their titles.

Next come the deans of the various colleges (arts, engineering, etc.), along with a couple of deans you may not have thought of before: dean of the faculty and dean of the graduate school. The dean of the faculty usually represents the interests of the faculty in relation to administrators and the board of trustees. The dean of the graduate school is most important to you because he or she has great sway over such matters as how many people are accepted into various graduate fields, how T.A.s are allocated by department, and what the requirements are for the PhD.

In small colleges, the administrative structure can be quite compressed; I know of some schools where there is a "president" who acts as president, provost, and vice-provost. The next officer in the chain is then the dean, of which there is only one. There is no need for a separate dean of faculty when a college has (say) forty faculty members, and of course, a college without a graduate program needs no dean of the graduate school.

After the associate and assistant deans of admissions, advising, and "dean of students," come the department chairs. Although elections may be held in departments, chairs serve at the behest of the dean. Thus, although a department faculty may vote to recommend a particular person, that vote is not binding on the dean.

Departments serve important functions. They determine their own courses of study, subject to college approval; they initiate the tenure process for faculty; they determine the requirements for the major and for graduation. Most importantly for you, departments admit graduate students and offer them financial aid.

Your department is very likely to have a director of graduate study (DGS) who oversees your academic life from start to finish. You will also have a thesis advisor, of course, but he or she will be much less involved in the administrative "paper trail."

So now we can figure out how you got a paycheck:

Last year, you applied to "the graduate school," which means that a secretary in the graduate school office opened and collected your application form and recommendation letters. Those materials were then sent from the graduate school office to another secretary in mathematics. That person handed them to a committee supervised by the DGS. After a lot of internal departmental deliberation, along with consultation with the dean of the graduate school about how much funding would be available this year, the committee chose you as one of its new students [Congratulations!]. At some institutions, this admission included an offer of support as a teaching assistant, in which case your letter of acceptance read something like, "You will receive full tuition and fees and a T.A. stipend worth [some amount of] dollars." Alternatively, you may have been offered admission, but told that T.A. support was pending "depending on graduate school funding." [Now you know what that sentence meant.]

A few months later, you showed up on campus, where you were immediately handed a flurry of forms to fill out ("I-9. What's that? Of course I'm a U.S. citizen.") by the same secretary who sent on your application to the DGS. (Now you know why that secretary looked at you as if you were an old friend.) You found out what your T.A. assignment was to be, and the secretary filled out more forms for the accounting and payroll offices. Two weeks later, what do you know! You got paid! Easy, right?

What Does An Evaluator Evaluate, Anyway?

I have been called on a number of times over the years to sit in on classes for the purposes of evaluating T.A.s and faculty. At first, I had no real idea of how to do this; I sat and listened, made a note or two and at the end said, "Thanks, nice class." I felt mildly uneasy about the whole system, but there didn't seem to be any role models for me to learn from or compare myself to. Only after a while did I start to develop my own techniques for dealing with the process.

Now when I am asked to evaluate a graduate student or faculty member, I first find out whether the evaluation is to be **formative** or **summative**.

A formative evaluation is one designed mainly to give the instructor and me a snapshot from that day. "How am I doing? What seems solid? What should I work on?" Then he or she can work toward the summative evaluation, the one that sometimes ends up in a letter of recommendation or a file in the deans' office.

I never consider a formative evaluation invasive. In fact, I like to invite colleagues to my class so as to get their opinion of how I'm doing, and because it makes summative evaluations of my own work easier to handle.

When I am asked to observe someone else's class, how do I begin? First, I make sure to ask the individual which day is best. There is no reason for me to show up on an exam day, for instance. On the other hand, there is good reason to attend when the lecturer is giving a lesson he or she is particularly enthusiastic about.

I come to class early, ask the instructor if it is still all right if I sit in (just in case plans have changed at the last minute), and then take a seat toward the back of the room. Although I prefer to be unobtrusive, students usually notice that I am in there, and I am aware that that fact sometimes changes the dynamic of the class.

I take notes as the class proceeds, recording the topic, the instructor's approach to it, and especially the dialogue that takes place:

Student: "I didn't get that last step." Instructor: "OK, I'll go back." When I see what might have been a missed opportunity for the instructor, I put a comment in brackets in the margin of the paper for later mention. I also record seemingly trivial facts, such as the time the class starts and the number of students the instructor has. If class starts late, that is a point to discuss later; if it is because of a late bus, that's one thing, but if it is part of a pattern that comes from the instructor's nervousness or dislike of teaching, then we have a matter for further discussion. If there are too few students in class, it may be because today is the day before semester break, or perhaps students are generally not coming to class because they see it as "useless."

After class, I ask the instructor if he or she would like to have some coffee and talk. I like to chat right after class, if possible, because the material is still fresh in our common memories. I always start with what I liked about the class, and I begin with the trivialities. "You speak loudly enough, and I like the way you wrote everything on the board so that students could take notes more easily." Many of the people I observe are better teachers than I was when I began, and I tell them so.

Then I move on to more serious issues. If students asked lots of questions, I consider that to be a real plus, because it shows that they are not cowed by the instructor even if he or she couldn't answer all the questions. I tell the instructor this fact; "It's good to see how you encourage the students to respond to the material by letting them ask you questions. I really liked the way that you were willing to field that question about [something you messed up]. It showed the students how you were thinking, even though you still need to work on the answer for next time."

If the instructor has done a good job with "mechanical skills," I then feel free to discuss deeper issues of teaching. Referring to my notes, I sometimes offer suggestions as to how to approach the classroom material from a more sophisticated perspective.

Here are some points that I have come to over time:

I classify teaching into three levels. At the first level, the instructor has an awareness of and an ability to handle the most basic aspects of teaching. He or she writes clearly, doesn't stand in front of the board, speaks loudly enough, comes to class fully prepared to discuss the assignments, treats students in a courteous manner, and understands and gives basic responses to questions asked in class. A new instructor should be able to learn these skills through a decent T.A. training program and to perfect them during the first semester of teaching.

A level two instructor is able to motivate the material being taught, perhaps by bringing in some relevant additional material, thinks well on his or her feet, is able to answer simple questions on lecture material and homework without difficulty, and is willing to spend some additional time with individual students.

At the third level, the instructor now knows what the student is "really asking" when he or she asks a particular question. This instructor can also say "where the course is going," and can give solid, coherent responses to questions of the "what's it all good for" variety. He or she acts professionally in all classroom situations.

Now let me return to the topic at hand. When I observe an instructor, I try to get an idea of which of the three levels he or she is on. My goal is then to reinforce good habits by complimenting this person on having attained the appropriate level (I don't say it this way, of course), and then to suggest one or two ways in which he or she can continue to get to the next level. I always use positive reinforcement and make suggestions built from what I have seen in the classroom. "I really like the way you were able to do all the problems the students asked. You were obviously prepared. By the way, remember that question twelve, the one about integrating the trigonometric function? I was noticing how you had a chance there to tell the students that they'd see those kinds of problems again if they take next semester's course."

I have occasionally had situations where the person I have evaluated has been, well, less than stellar. Each of these was different, and of course I need to preserve confidentiality, but I will try to describe some of these because they are relevant. In each of the stories below, I am going to describe the individual as a male.

One instructor reacted so much to my presence in his classroom that he basically stopped trying to teach the students and instead spent most of his time convincing me that he knew the proofs behind the material he was covering. In this case, I told him after class what I thought he had done — he agreed — and suggested that I "forget this one" and come back in a couple of weeks to see a more typical class. That later lesson went much better and I was able to write a nice recommendation for him.

A second case involved a first-semester instructor from another country. Although he knew how to do the homework problems that had been assigned, when the students asked for further details, he would launch again into the previous explanation, thus making the students upset. I broke my rule of noninterference and actually stopped the class in the last few minutes. I then explained to the students that I thought the instructor was just a little nervous. "He really does know the answers — see, he's doing the problems very well [this comment relaxed the instructor a bit], he's simply having some problem getting used to the American accent." This, too, turned out to be true. I said that the students' frustrations should not be with the instructor, they should be with me, the person who put him into the class right after he had arrived from another culture. I then asked the students to speak more slowly, and to ask more focused questions; e.g., "I followed you until you got to the step about factoring, and then I lost you." This worked so well that by the end of the semester the instructor's evaluations were near the top of the scale. Further, that instructor later blossomed into one of my best.

Yet the previous solution did not work in a similar situation. The instructor was so confused by being in front of a class of "standard Americans" that I had to remove him from the classroom for further language training. I did assure him, however, that there would come a day when he would reenter "and you will be much more prepared then than you were today." He was, to say the least, relieved. Although his abilities did not increase markedly over the course of his career, at least we had tried to help him in his teaching.

I had a case some years ago where the instructor was belligerent. If students asked him questions, he would belittle them: "You're supposed to know this; don't ask me how to solve the problem, how did **you** do it?" Meanwhile, he would not necessarily solve the homework problems correctly himself. I took him to my office to discuss the situation with him, explaining that he needed to work harder on his own assignments, on his method of answering questions, and especially on his attitude. Then, when I observed him a few weeks later and found that he had not improved in any of the above categories, I was able to issue him a warning that "…if I don't see substantive improvement this semester" in the aforementioned ways, he would not be rehired. Unfortunately, he did not improve, and unfortunately, he was not rehired. Thus I learned again, if I didn't know already, that not every person is cut out for teaching, and not every case leads on to success. But I also kept that instructor from making the next semester's class miserable.

The vast majority of the instructors I have evaluated have not been of this last type, however. Most want to make teaching an integral part of their life's work, and they accept formative evaluation as a significant means of improvement in their careers.

I'd like to point out that some people strongly dislike being evaluated, and most people have problems with some aspects of evaluation (see the Course Evaluation section for some of my own complaints), yet the process can be constructed so as to be a helpful one. Since more and more schools are requesting accountability from their faculty, there is a reasonably high possibility that you will be asked to go through an evaluation. You can help make this a more salutary one by realizing that it is ultimately designed to help you. After all, your students are watching you all the time, and their critical faculties are not turned off; why not let a colleague watch you, too? He or she may be able to say just what you need to improve your teaching to level three — and beyond.

Becoming a Faculty Member

For you as graduate student, the prospect of getting a faculty position at a college or university may seem like entry into paradise, and to an extent it is. But before you decide that being a faculty member is all wonderful, let me explain some of the new challenges you will encounter.

The relief you will feel from having found a job will be almost immediately supplanted by a sense of aloneness, insecurity and avoidance.

Right now as a graduate student you have a cohort of other "n^{th} years" who are going through roughly the same crucible as you are. Now, however, the other person who was hired at the same time as you may well see him- or herself as vying for the lone tenure slot. Your conversations will become guarded, if they exist at all. The older faculty, at the same time, will seem distant. Maybe it's because they have their own problems to contend with, maybe they are "just quiet," and maybe it *really* is because you replaced the person they wanted to have hired. In any event, you may be spending a lot of commuting time in the mornings and evenings trying to "psych out" other people's motivations.

It helps to keep telling yourself that the institution you are going to has already made a real investment in you — they do want you to succeed, even if it doesn't seem so at times. Try to ignore what seem to be snubs, and keep to the track of doing what's best for your students and for mathematics. Save your disagreements for extremely significant issues, whatever those may be. Build a coterie of colleagues with whom you can work, share ideas, talk about mathematics, and, most importantly, go to lunch with or to the gym.

Speaking of investments, you will probably think that the fact that you are now earning about three times what you made as a T.A. makes you rich. Well, you're not as rich as you thought, because your deductions from income for taxes and social security, for your medical benefits, for your retirement forty years hence, and maybe even for your campus parking place, will probably take about forty percent of that paycheck. That still leaves you with almost double what you had as a T.A. But wait! You forgot that you used to live in "collegetown" with four roommates, and that too is going to change. Not to mention the car you'll buy to fill up the parking place you're paying for, right?

Since you are new to the institution, you won't know (and sometimes you won't *respect*) the campus culture. If you are careful and politic, you will have an opportunity to redirect the culture — within reason. But first you must build the confidence of others:

- You must listen before offering advice,
- You must make realistic suggestions that come out of the current modes of operation, and
- You must be willing to accept criticism or correction.

Remember, your new colleagues can very quickly get tired of hearing you say, "When I was at Famous U. we did it this way...."

At your new institution, you will be evaluated based on the quality of your **research** and **scholarship**, your **teaching**, and your **service**.

Research is the topic that you as a young faculty member without tenure think about first. After all, you have just come from a university where your advisor, your committee, your chair, your officemate and your significant other all wanted to know when you were going to get that thesis done. In theory, then, you should be perfectly primed to take care of all the details of keeping up your research program, right?

Wrong!

There are real impediments to doing research at your new institution:

- You never did this alone before.
- You don't have the graduate seminar to keep you active now.
- The library facilities aren't nearly as good.
- Colleagues aren't working in your area any more.
- You need to spend much more time on classes, preparation, grading, committees, and so forth.

How do you get out of this bind?

Self-management is **essential**.

A) Put yourself on a schedule. Stick to it. Here's mine from last semester.

	M	Tue	Wed	Thurs	Fri
8–10	Plan lesson	Write	Plan lesson	Write	Plan lesson
10–11	e-mail, admin	D.H.'s class	e-mail, admin	D.H.'s class	e-mail, admin
11–12	Math 453	Run	453	Run	453
1–3	Write	Seminar	Plan lesson	Write	Run
3–4	Run	Office hours	Office hours		Brian G.'s class
4–6	OccSem	Seminar	M500	Seminar	

B) Consider changing research topics toward ones more like colleagues'. Of course, there are real questions here: Should you "soldier on" with the topic that brought you the thesis and the job, or should you move into a new field with its uncertainty of results? How far is the new field from what you already know? How many papers can you generate before the tenure decision is made? How interesting and how promising is this new field?

C) Don't waste all of Friday afternoons ($2 \times 30 = 60$ hours), Sunday evenings ($2 \times 30 = 60$ hours), spring breaks ($9 \times 6 = 54$ hours), summers ($12 \times 30 = 360$), those reading weeks the students have before exams ($20 \times 2 = 40$ hours), and the like. The hours add up to 574 hours, and that equals 14.6 weeks of work!

D) Talk to other faculty ("mentors") who have had success. How did they do it? Also, remember that you can choose your own mentors; not every one needs to be formally assigned. For instance, I know a faculty member who would simply sit with a group of people who were willing to "share their concerns" with her at lunch.

E) Don't let teaching and service take over. Don't ignore them, but don't let them take over.

F) Make your own set of priorities. Find out the college's "rules" for tenure, and follow them. (I'll return to this point later.)

I could say more, but now let me move on to **scholarship**.

Once upon a time, research was all-important. Recently, the word scholarship has come to be more emphasized, and the more educationally oriented types of work have come to be recognized as activity worthy of consideration for tenure.

The Boyer commission and Carnegie Foundation (reference [6]) have been working to broaden direction, especially for the schools not classified as "Research I" institutions, from the traditional model to one of scholarship. Your response may be "So what?" But deans and provosts are cognizant of this change of paradigm. What does it mean?

It means that schools following the Boyer model have an expanded view of "research." A paper in the *Proceedings* is still great, but for this school so is the work you did with a sociologist, where you did the statistical work for her data. A copy of your thesis in the *Transactions* is obviously wonderful, but so is a description of your new "geometry for the liberal arts" course in *College Teaching*. Your talk at the high school's math day is scholarship, as is your twenty-minute talk at the MAA sectional meeting.

You should consider this expansive view of scholarly activity as an opportunity for you to show off your skills and put the college in the forefront. Take advantage of such an opportunity; don't think of it as "just another way the dean is trying to get work out of me." Well, to quote that great philosopher, Homer Simpson, "D'oh!"

As tuition has increased on college campuses, **teaching** has also become more important; more students and parents ask, "What am I getting for all this money?" This is one reason why it is important for you, as a graduate student, to get as varied a set of T.A. assignments as possible, and to take teaching issues seriously before you get to your tenure-stream position and tenure-question problems.

Teaching is central to the mission of every college. You can be cynical and make claims that it doesn't matter at your school, but it does. If your sections of calculus are consistently smaller than everyone else's, that fact will be noted, even if you maintain that you're "just upholding standards," and that "these students aren't any good, anyway." If your course evaluations are low enough that the chair points them out on your performance review, watch out. If students are writing comments about you on bathroom walls, look out!

Of course, mathematics has a reputation for being a difficult and unpopular subject (after all, this is a field where "I still hate math, but he sort of made me understand it" is considered praise) but do you have to make yourself difficult and unpopular as a person?

Look, this is the job you will be working at for the next thirty or forty years. Why not derive some pleasure from it? Why not care, at least a bit, about how you teach calculus? How about engendering some interest on the part of precalculus students? Why not design a nice course for liberal arts majors?

Some topics to consider in your teaching:

- Audience — What works for engineers doesn't necessarily do so for arts students.

- Assignments — Too hard? Too easy? Too vague? Too many?

- Quizzes and Exams — Same questions as above.

- "Standards" — Think about why is it that some instructors can't seem to spell out what they want of the students. Is it always wrong that some exams are "just like the homework?"

Some more advice:

Talk to colleagues. They have been there.

Talk to the learning resource center and the faculty development people. Yes, mathematics is "different," but it is also a human endeavor and good development people have approaches to expanding students' minds that just might work for you.

What you may have learned in this short book is not enough; read more about Bloom's model of cognition and Perry's model of development. Ask yourself, "What is it I want students to get? How can I best achieve this goal? And, what classroom models am I seeing that best fit my aims?" [I, for instance, don't teach topology the way I do calculus.]

Use evaluations; don't just tabulate them. If the comment is "Math sucks!" who cares; forget it. If, on the other hand, it's "He's not always as well-prepared as I wish he was," then that's very worthy of consideration.

Another word about evaluations; they are serious, but not fatal. If things are going wrong, invite a friendly colleague into your class, and accept suggestions, but don't just throw away all your techniques just because someone else you admire does things differently. Develop a style that comes from *your own* personality, not from the latest trends. Not everyone is best suited for "cooperative learning," for instance.

Let me repeat something I said in another chapter of this book, just in case this is the only chapter you read: I don't think I know what "great teaching" is, but I firmly believe that "good teaching" can be taught. Here are some aspects:

1. Choose a "decent" book. If the choice isn't yours, don't complain inordinately. The students will always see the choice as yours, and they will not be sympathetic.

2. Get old syllabi. Work from them. Know what the college catalog says is required. No excuses are acceptable for your skipping an essential topic.

3. Prepare, and do so actively. You cannot know everything, but you can understand the broad outlines of the topics in the book.

4. Test at the level of the text, your lectures and the classroom discussion. If the text is "too easy," you can augment it *somewhat*. But be careful; what is easy for you isn't necessarily the same for the students.

5. Have some fun. Don't leave your personality at home. At the same time, remember that the students see you as an authority figure, not a slightly older pal. You are grading them, and they know it.

I could spend the rest of the day on teaching issues. Instead, let's talk a bit about **service**.

Service has often been a misunderstood criterion for tenure. There are some schools that consider the presidency of the local runners' club as "service," but for the most part, colleges interpret the word to mean work in your specialty. Thus if you are a math educator who gets elected to the school board, that's service, because it is a good place to learn about such ideas as how secondary education fits with college. The word also refers to committee work in your department or at the college level. For instance, if you are on your school's bylaws committee, you are promoting collegiality.

Service has many meanings. After all, most of what the dean does is really service; for instance, reading your tenure file is part of that. Service *is* important, and others do evaluate it. If you do not take it seriously, people on the tenure and promotion committee will hear about that fact.

Let me discuss one more underappreciated aspect of the topic: Service is the type of work that others in the community will most readily observe. Thus you should come to meetings well prepared, perform your assigned duties and make informed judgements. Offer opinions, but expect to have to revise them because of additional information. Also expect to sometimes lose arguments.

Above all, **be a colleague**. Ideally, you will be at your institution for thirty or forty more years; now is the time to start making lifetime friends. Of course, that last does not mean that you have to like and trust everyone — you don't leave your critical skills in your desk, do you?

The Essence of Good Teaching

It is commonplace to hear some people say, "You can't teach teaching. It's ingrained." In fact, I just heard this last week from a faculty member in another discipline. While I agree, to some extent, about teaching being ingrained, as part of one's personality, I can't agree that teaching cannot be taught.

Maybe it's because I have been trying to "teach people how to teach" for over fifteen years now, but I do believe that some aspects of instruction are definitely teachable. For instance, if you go back to the previous section, What Does An Evaluator Evaluate, Anyway?, you will see that there I talk about levels one, two and three of teaching. Certainly, such level one aspects as speaking loudly, writing clearly, not standing in front of the material on the board, coming to class prepared, and treating students with respect are all teachable. In fact, many people would say that those attributes are such common sense that they need not be taught — but we have all seen too many instructors who seem to have skipped that lesson. My belief is that all the level one aspects can be taught during a one-week T.A. training session, and then reinforced throughout the first semester's teaching so that they become close to second nature.

Further, I would contend that level two aspects can also be taught. When I look at these qualities, however, I do not see "common sense" principles, but rather teaching traits that must be developed over a period of time, through teaching itself, but also through mentoring, peer suggestion, and perhaps also through taking some teaching courses. Unfortunately, college teaching courses seem to be a rarity these days — we must hope that they will grow in number.

So simple teaching, "good teaching," I would claim, is teachable. Any graduate student who uses his or her time in graduate school can become a better than adequate college-level instructor. There, I said it, and I'll say it again: Good teaching *is* teachable.

"Great" teaching; now that's something else. Although to me *some* aspects of greatness are approachable by us mere mortals, there is also a sense in which teaching is an expression of personality, and just as some of us don't really want to be stock brokers, others simply aren't geared up for teaching. Is this bad? I don't think so, unless we find ourselves having to teach in order to live; in that case, I still think we should "give it our best, and not apologize for our supposed shortcomings."

I know that I myself was an incredibly shy child who never wanted to be called on to recite, and at times I still have more-than-normal problems with the concept of standing in front of an audience. Yet, I have managed to teach classes of up to five hundred undergraduate students and give serious mathematical lectures to working research mathematicians (usually the latter is easier than the former). But I think that I can do so only by wrapping myself completely in the mathematics. Early in my career, I used to try to memorize every detail of my lecture, hoping, I guess, to fool people into thinking that I knew all about the material. That would work only as long as I never had to look at my notes; once I did have to peek, it was all over for any "quality exposition." Later on, I realized that I could use transparencies, notes, even full text, whatever it takes to get my point across, and that by always trying to use my memory I was often depriving my audience of the gist of my talks.

Some people have told me that it is possible to find a model of good teaching in those who have taught us well in the past. Well, maybe. I recall some people who taught me well; while they have definitely shown me many things about teaching, and about their fields of study, they didn't seem to conform to any single mold.

One of the first college instructors I had, and whom I thought was "gifted," broke most of the rules I might try to enunciate. I won't give you his name or his school, for reasons that will be clear from my description. First, Professor E., an English professor, would "drink his lunch," as we used to say. Then he would start a seventy-five minute class at 1:30 in the afternoon with a thirty- to forty-minute standup comedy routine with no basis in the classroom readings or discussion. At some point in the routine, he would stop, sigh, pull out some old, yellowed papers from a severely beaten up briefcase, and say to the assembled multitude, "Well, I guess I have to say something about Hawthorne. Don't feel you have to listen; you can go to sleep now, if you wish." Then he would proceed to offer a careful, lucid analysis of *The Scarlet Letter* and its implications for Hawthorne's life and the sociology of early New England. To me, that analysis was the reason I came to class; Professor E. was serious, engaged in the material, centered in eighteenth century literature in ways that other instructors were not. Maybe other students came to class for the witticisms of an irascible old man (ten years younger, by the way, than I am as I write this), but what I saw was a scholar at work.

Just in case you think that Professor E. was uniquely sensitive to students' or the community's concerns, I'll just point out that he told us one day in class that he stayed in our backwater town only because, "as I have told the faculty many times, this is a place to which culture is coming. Although when, I don't know."

Another professor at a different school, a mathematician, was incredibly shy; when he wasn't teaching, he seemed incapable of conversation. Yet, when in class, he gave the kind of mathematical talk that made every student sure that he or she understood every detail — until we tried to do the exercises. When we would come to ask him about the problems we were stuck on, he would say, "Oh yes, that one got me for a while, too. Let's see if we can figure it out again." Professor M. was an incredible motivator who allowed us into his mind. He took apart proofs as if they were watches and then put each piece back together exactly where it should go.

A third instructor was a stickler for proofs in an engineering calculus course. Somehow, he was able to convince the engineering students that "You need proofs to understand why things work; otherwise your bridges won't stand up!" And, he had the force of personality to make his opinion stick. Thus, when he took the class through the difference between a hypothesis and a conclusion, when he showed us by examples how each hypothesis was necessary to the proof, when he counted hypotheses in his proofs, we listened, and listened carefully — and not only because the material was going to be on the exam.

What have I learned from these instructors? Well, definitely not that I should drink to excess before going to class. Nor do I do standup comedy for my class; although I do sometimes exhibit a sense of humor, I can't remember, let alone tell, a canned joke under any circumstance. While I am shy, I don't walk around hoping that people will not talk to me, nor do I try to convince engineers that proofs are "where it's at."

I guess what I have learned from all this is that great teaching comes in all forms, but that mainly it comes from the delicate interaction between two personalities: that of the instructor who somehow conveys a love of learning and the student who comes ready to absorb and apply what the instructor has to give — no matter how imperfect that instructor may be outside his or her domain of expertise.

Case Studies

Introduction

In the next few pages, I present some bare bones case studies that I have used over the years. I do not offer any of the classroom or corridor discussions that have resulted from these, but that is not because these conversations have not been stimulating.

I have two reasons for not providing commentary:

- Each semester, at least one of these case studies generates comments that I would have never thought of, and

- Younger T.A.s are especially inclined to think of the discussion as "The Answer" to how these situations should be treated.

This is not to say that I don't favor certain approaches to selected cases, but I really don't think that there is a single correct response to very many of these stories.

My methodology for using these case studies in the classroom is to read them aloud and then let others dive in right away. On those occasions when I have suggested that people take some of them home to think about before "the next class," I have usually found that they stay around to start a discussion of their favorites right away; so I figure, "Why not have the commentary now?"

For those of you who wish to make notes of your own responses or of the classroom discussion, I have left plenty of space. If you have questions or comments, or if you want to suggest some case studies of your own, please contact me. Some of my favorite cases have come from coffee lounge conversations about teaching.

Case Study I

You have arranged your calculus class so that you collect homework in class each week for grading. You have told students that ten percent of their final grade will come from these assignments. After five weeks of the semester, you find out that complete homework sets are sold in the campus bookstore, and that they are also available in the library. What do you do about this? Do you change your grading policy? Do you stop collecting homework? Do you give credit for homework that you have already collected?

How do you change your examination and grading policy for the next semester? Should you try to change department or university policy about what kinds of books and course materials are sold in the campus bookstore?

I wouldn't change grading policy, or class routine, and I would accept the previous homework. Instead, I would change the assignments, assigning some problems that weren't in the homework sets sold in the bookstore.
For the following semester, I would continue this process, unless the second semester's homework wasn't in the bookstore or library. In this case, I would see if it's possible to change university policy.

Case Study II

Assume, for the sake of argument (it may even be true), that you are a female T.A. You have been assigned an overwhelmingly male class of calculus students who are, to say the least, rather boisterous. One student in particular has a tendency to mention your clothes, your hair, your personal appearance at or near the start of class every day. How do you respond? Do you publicly reprimand the student in class? Do you change your manner of dress? Do you change your behavior? Do you ask the lecturer to intervene?

Exactly what is going on in class, and how do you handle it?

I wouldn't change anything about my behavior or appearance. This would just encourage more comments. I would speak with the lecturer regarding the school's policy on sexual harassment, and then perhaps speak with the student personally and warn him that I will take action along those lines if he continues. This would certainly solve the problem.

what about the other way around?

Case Study III A

You are proctoring an exam. You notice that Student A is looking at someone in the row ahead of him, but that the person he is looking at seems too far away for him to be copying. Occasionally during the exam, you go back to the general area where the students are sitting, but you see nothing unusual from either him or from Students B and C sitting one row ahead and about six and eight seats away. At the end of the exam, you take Student A aside and mention that he shouldn't spend so much time "looking around." He responds, "Didn't you see what was going on? Those students were cheating! I want you to take them to the judicial administrator, and I want to testify!"

How do you respond? What do you do about the situation? Do you take the case to the judicial administrator? Do you have Student A testify?

Case Study III B

You took Case Study IIIA to the judicial administrator. Sure enough there was cheating going on, which you were able to prove by using copies of the exams. You did not ask Student A to testify. Student B admitted "looking over" the exam booklet of Student C, but Students B and C both claimed that Student C was not a participant in the malfeasance. Student A comes to ask about the outcome, and when he finds out that Student C has not been convicted, he is again upset. "But she was involved, too! She was showing him the answers!"

Now what do you do?

Case Study IV

It is Sunday night; the second exam in your second-semester calculus class is scheduled for Tuesday. You are in the middle of a review session for three of the sections of the class. After an hour's worth of student questions, you realize that your answers are not getting through. Students do not understand power series, a topic that will surely be on the exam. On Monday you are supposed to go on to a new topic, so you feel some time pressure – after all, the next exam will also be important.

What can you do to help the students prepare for this exam? Should you simply ignore the syllabus? How could you do this without incurring the wrath of the course leader?

Case Study V

On Tuesday you decide to go to a movie on campus. While standing in line with your roommate, you meet one of your students. You begin a conversation, which you continue in the theatre. Two days later, the T.A. coordinator receives a dyspeptic letter from another student in the class. The letter writer says that you were "out on a date" with one of your students, that the student you were with is "the soon- to-be former" boy- or girlfriend of the letter writer, that you "are trying to break up the relationship," and that the T.A. coordinator should not tell you about the letter because you will just try to fail her or him in the class, "…which you've been trying to do all term anyway."

The T.A. coordinator calls you in anyway to "discuss the situation." What do you do?

Case Study VI

You hear from one of your students that one of the other T.A.s in your large-lecture class is "favoring his own students." In particular, your student claims that "the other T.A. is changing grades for his own students but not for others, and he actually showed his students how to solve two of the exam problems before they appeared on the test the other night."

How do you handle this complaint? Should you confront the other T.A.? How do you verify the accusations? Can you verify them? Should you verify them?

Case Study VII

You are conducting a review session for tomorrow night's exam. One of the students asks you to solve a problem that you know will be on the test. What do you do?

Case Study VIII

During your discussion of final grades, the instructor you are working with announces a new grading policy: no student can have a final grade raised unless another student's grade is lowered by an equivalent amount. You immediately think about one of your undergraduates who spent two weeks in the hospital recovering from surgery. She then got a terrible grade on the next exam, but righted herself enough to score 97% on the final. Should you give her the A you think she deserves, even if this means finding another student whose grade will have to be lowered from, say, a B to a C? Should you just forget changing any grades? Or, should you argue with the instructor about his grading policy, and if so, what do you say?

Case Study IX

You are T.A.ing another large lecture course. At the final grading discussion, the faculty member in charge announces his "ironclad policy" that no student with less than 490 points out of 500 is to be given a grade of A^+. You have a student who received 486 points, but who would have done better except that she had a death in the family. You decide to give her an A^+ anyway, which you do without consultation with the "czar."

Two days later, another student from the class comes to see you. "I got 488 points, higher than my roommate, to whom you gave an A^+. I demand an A^+, too, and I intend to fight this through the administration if you don't give me one."

Now what do you do?

Case Study X

It is week three of the semester, and your class has shrunk from twenty-five to nine. You happen to see one of your former students outside the cafeteria; he seems not to want to talk about it. After some prodding, he says, "It was your accent," then he walks away.

What do you do? Do you think it was your accent? What else could the problem be? Where can you go for advice? Should you discuss the situation with your class? With fellow T.A.s? With an instructor?

Case Study XI

You have won one of the college's T.A. teaching awards. Your response is happy, but also ambivalent. It is nice that your students like your teaching, but at the same time you feel your teaching isn't that special. As you pass the coffee room, you hear another T.A. saying loudly, "Yeah, but he's just an actor. It's all show."

What do you think? Is it all show? Are you "just a performer?" And, how much of teaching should be performance?

Case Study XII A

You inadvertently discover that your course leader has been making personal copies, using departmental mailing privileges, and taking supplies for his own use.

What do you do? Do you confront the course leader? Do you take the matter to the chair? Or do you simply "ignore" the situation?

Case Study XII B

You discover that one of your students is accusing your course leader of harassment. The accusations have circulated through the dormitories, but the accuser has not made a formal complaint.

What do you do? Do you take the matter to the chair? Do you just "ignore" the situation?

Case XII C

One of your students comes to you to complain that the course leader is a harasser. The student, obviously upset, wants your advice as to what to do. What do you suggest to the student? Where do you take the case from here?

Case XIII

One of your students has been rather aggressive in your classes. For example, she always wants her problems solved first. When you begin to answer, she often interrupts to say, "That doesn't make sense!" She feels free to interrupt other students, too; when you once showed her how to do a problem, she responded, "You don't give enough details! You're not helping me at all!" Then, if you work a problem she isn't interested in, she puts her head down on the desk and acts as if she's asleep. However, sometimes after class she comes to ask details of one or two of the problems she showed disinterest in.

How do you handle this situation? Do you berate her for her behavior? Ask her to leave class? Send her to a counselor? Talk to her after class? Get other students involved?

Case Study XIV

Between looking for jobs and writing your thesis, you have just been too busy to plan for your calculus class. You got away with winging it last week, after you returned from an on-campus interview. Today, however, here you stand in front of a class full of sophomore engineers, and you can't remember how to solve the Stokes' Theorem problem. You have just wasted twenty minutes on the question, and both you and the students are clearly getting annoyed and frustrated, what with the exam coming up tomorrow evening.

With five minutes to go in class, what do you say? What do you do now? How do you order your priorities better in the future? After all, the thesis and the job market are important too, aren't they?

Case Study XV

Professor Smith, the overseer of the course you are T.A. for, puts an arm around you in the office and tells you that, if your advisor isn't "taking care of you, you just come to me and I'll help you out."

Have you been propositioned? What should you do about this situation?

References

1. Angelo, Thomas and K. Cross. *Classroom Assessment Techniques*. San Francisco: Jossey-Bass, 1993.

2. Belenky, M.F., B. Clenchy, N. Goldberger and J. Torule. *Women's Ways of Knowing: The Development of Self, Voice and Mind*. New York: Basic Books, 1986.

3. Bloom, Benjamin, ed. *Taxonomy of Educational Objectives*. New York: Longmans, Green, 1952.

4. Bonwell, Charles and J. Eison. *Active Learning: Creating Excitement in the Classroom*. Washington: George Washington University, 1991.

5. Boyer, Carl and Uta Merzbach. *A History of Mathematics*. New York: Wiley, 1989.

6. Boyer, Ernest. *Scholarship Reconsidered*. San Francisco: Jossey-Bass, 1990.

7. Chaffee, John. *Thinking Critically*. Boston: Houghton Mifflin, 1997.

8. Cohen, Marcus et al. *Student Research Projects in Calculus*. Washington: The Mathematical Association of America, 1991.

9. Countryman, Joan. *Writing to Learn Mathematics*. Portsmouth, NH: Heinemann, 1992.

10. Culver, R. S. and J. Hackos. "Perry's model of intellectual development," *Engr. Educ.* 73, 221.

11. DeNeef, Leigh and C. Goodwin, eds. *The Academic's Handbook*. Durham: Duke, 1995.

12. Eble, Kenneth. *The Craft of Teaching*. San Francisco: Jossey-Bass, 1988.

13. Edwards, C. H. *The Historical Development of the Calculus*. New York: Springer-Verlag, 1979.

14. Hagelgans, Nancy L., et al. *A Practical Guide to Cooperative Learning in Collegiate Mathematics*. MAA Math Notes 37. Washington: The Mathematical Association of America, 1995.

15. Highet, Gilbert. *The Art of Teaching*. New York: Vintage, 1977.

16. Hilbert, Steven et al. *Calculus: An Active Approach with Projects*. New York: Wiley, 1994.

17. Jackson, Michael and J. Ramsey, eds. *Problems for Student Investigation.* Washington: The Mathematical Association of America, 1993.

18. Karian, Zaven, ed. *Symbolic Computation in Undergraduate Mathematics Education.* MAA Math Notes 24. Washington: The Mathematical Association of America, 1992.

19. Kline, Morris. *Mathematical Thought from Ancient to Modern Times.* New York: Oxford, 1972.

20. Lewin, Myrtle and T. Rishel. "Support Systems in Beginning Calculus." *PRIMUS.* V(3). 275-86.

21. McKeachie, W. *Teaching Tips.* Lexington, MA: D.C. Heath, 1994.

22. Meier, John and T. Rishel. *Writing in the Teaching and Learning of Mathematics.* MAA Math Notes 48. Washington: The Mathematical Association of America, 1998.

23. Perry, William. *Forms of Intellectual and Ethical Development in the College Years: A Scheme.* New York: Holt, Rinehart and Winston, 1970.

24. Piaget, Jean. *The Child's Conception of Number.* London: Routledge and Paul, 1952.

25. Pólya, George. *How to Solve It.* Princeton, 1945.

26. Rishel, Thomas. "Writing in the Math Classroom, Math in the Writing Class; or How I Spent My Summer Vacation." *Using Writing to Teach Mathematics,* ed. A. Sterrett. MAA Math Notes 16. Washington: The Mathematical Association of America, 1992.

27. Sterrett, Andrew, ed. *Using Writing to Teach Mathematics.* Washington: The Mathematical Association of America, 1992.

28. Stewart, James. *Calculus: Concepts and Contexts.* Pacific Grove, CA: ITP, 1997.

29. Thomas, George and R. Finney. *Calculus and Analytic Geometry.* Reading, MA: Addison-Wesley, 1996.

30. Vygotsky, Lev. *Thought and Language.* Cambridge: MIT Press, 1986.

Appendix A

NUTS AND BOLTS QUESTIONNAIRE

The choices that you circle below will provide useful information for your instructor to enable her/him to improve your classroom experience. If you have concerns or questions that would not be addressed by this questionnaire, the Mathematics Department invites you to discuss these with our Associate Chair.

My speaking voice is:	too quiet	just right	too loud
I speak:	too fast	right speed	slowly
Understanding my pronunciation is:	difficult	fair	easy
Understanding my grammar is:	difficult	fair	easy
I tend to block the board:	too often	sometimes	seldom
I tend to erase the board too quickly:	yes	occasionally	no
My writing is:	too small	right size	too big
Reading my handwriting is:	difficult	fair	easy
Understanding my graphs & diagrams is:	difficult	fair	easy
I cover material:	too quickly	right speed	too slowly
The level of detail presented is:	too little	just right	too much
Time spent on homework in class & recitation is:	too little	right amount	too much
I cover the required material:	inadequately	adequately	very well
I tend to get sidetracked:	too easily	sometimes	seldom
I am able to answer questions in class:	no	somewhat	yes
My organization of presented material is:	poor	fair	good
The amount of material prepared is:	too little	just right	too much
I appear to be:	bored	responsive	enthusiastic
I seek and answer questions:	too seldom	right amount	too often
I recognize when the class is confused:	no	sometimes	yes
Are you embarrassed to ask questions:	yes	somewhat	no
I direct my teaching to:	a select few	majority	entire class
The level of class participation is:	too little	right	too much
I am approachable outside of class for help:	no	somewhat	yes
I maintain adequate classroom control:	no	sometimes	yes
My office hours are publicized:	poorly	adequately	well
I adhere to office hours:	seldom	sometimes	always
Homework is returned on time:	never	sometimes	always
Homework grading is:	inconsistent	adequate	helpful
The computer labs are relevant and useful:	no	somewhat	yes

Appendix B

Project 1
Applications of Integration with sin and cos
Matt Horak

Due date: Friday, February 18

Overview: This is a two section project. The sections have the common theme of the uses in calculus for trignometric functions, especially $\sin(x)$ and $\cos(x)$. In the first section, we compute the area of a circle. At first glance, it would not seem that $\sin(x)$ and $\cos(x)$ would play any role in evaluating the integral required for finding this area. But, as we shall see, those two functions have a tendency to be very useful in places where, initially, one would not expect them to show up. In the second section, we see that sin and cos relate to each other in an important way. In order to solve these problems, you will be required to exercise your skills with trigonometric identities and the techniques of integration that we have learned this semester.

Section 1: Computing the area of a circle.

In this section you will prove the well known fact that the area, A, of a circle of radius r is given by $A = \pi r^2$. You will use integration and a new technique for evaluating integrals known as *trigonometric substitution*.

A) We know that the equation for a circle of radius r centered at $(0,0)$ is $x^2 + y^2 = r^2$. Using this information, write an equation $y = f(x)$ for the graph of the part of this circle which lies above the x–axis. Graph this equation.

B) Write an expression (an integral) for the area between this curve and the x–axis.

C) Relate this area to A, the area of the circle given by $x^2 + y^2 = r^2$.

D) Now, write an expression for the area under $f(x)$ and in the first quadrant (the upper right quarter of the plane), and relate this integral to A.

E) As you can see, this equation might enable us to compute A. The first step is solving for A. Do this now.

If everything went correctly, you should have

$$A = 4 \int_0^r \sqrt{r^2 - x^2}\, dx.$$

We will use trignometric substitution to evaluate this. This method works with many types of integrals, and the idea is that we have a lot of trigonometric identities at our disposal (see pages A24 and A25 in our text), and we would like to use them to simplify the expression inside an integral. This is usually done by setting x equal to $a \sin \theta$, $a \tan \theta$ or some other trig function. Then one computes dx and rewrites the given integral in terms of θ. In our case, $r \sin \theta$ is one substitution that works.

F) Make the substitution $x = r \sin \theta$ and rewrite $\int_0^r \sqrt{r^2 - x^2}\, dx$ in terms of θ (Watch your limits!).

G) After that step, the piece under your square root sign looks like it is a good candidate for simplification using a trigonometric identity you know (or can look up in the back of the book). Simplify this as much as possible, showing each step.

Project 1
Applications of Integration with sin and cos
Matt Horak

Due date: Friday, February 18

Overview: This is a two section project. The sections have the common theme of the uses in calculus for trignometric functions, especially $\sin(x)$ and $\cos(x)$. In the first section, we compute the area of a circle. At first glance, it would not seem that $\sin(x)$ and $\cos(x)$ would play any role in evaluating the integral required for finding this area. But, as we shall see, those two functions have a tendency to be very useful in places where, initially, one would not expect them to show up. In the second section, we see that sin and cos relate to each other in an important way. In order to solve these problems, you will be required to exercise your skills with trignometric identities and the techniques of integration that we have learned this semester.

Section 1: Computing the area of a circle.

In this section you will prove the well known fact that the area, A, of a circle of radius r is given by $A = \pi r^2$. You will use integration and a new technique for evaluating integrals known as *trignometric substitution*.

A) We know that the equation for a circle of radius r centered at $(0,0)$ is $x^2 + y^2 = r^2$. Using this information, write an equation $y = f(x)$ for the graph of the part of this circle which lies above the x–axis. Graph this equation.

B) Write an expression (an integral) for the area between this curve and the x–axis.

C) Relate this area to A, the area of the circle given by $x^2 + y^2 = r^2$.

D) Now, write an expression for the area under $f(x)$ and in the first quadrant (the upper right quarter of the plane), and relate this integral to A.

E) As you can see, this equation might enable us to compute A. The first step is solving for A. Do this now.

If everything went correctly, you should have

$$A = 4 \int_0^r \sqrt{r^2 - x^2}\,dx.$$

We will use trigonometric substitution to evaluate this. This method works with many types of integrals, and the idea is that we have a lot of trigonometric identities at our disposal (see pages A24 and A25 in our text), and we would like to use them to simplify the expression inside an integral. This is usually done by setting x equal to $a \sin\theta$, $a \tan\theta$ or some other trig function. Then one computes dx and rewrites the given integral in terms of θ. In our case, $r \sin\theta$ is one substitution that works.

F) Make the substitution $x = r \sin\theta$ and rewrite $\int_0^r \sqrt{r^2 - x^2}\,dx$ in terms of θ (Watch your limits!).

G) After that step, the piece under your square root sign looks like it is a good candidate for simplification using a trigonometric identity you know (or can look up in the back of the book). Simplify this as much as possible, showing each step.

B) Using the same kind of method as in A) prove that

$$\int_{-\pi}^{\pi} \sin(mx)\cos(mx)dx = 0$$

where m is an integer.

C) Now, to get a feel for the next proof, we will start out with a concrete example: find

$$G(x) = \int \sin(2x)\cos(x)dx$$

and use $G(x)$ to calculate $\int_{-\pi}^{\pi} \sin(2x)\cos(x)dx$. You will probably find a trignometric identity handy in finding $G(x)$.

D) Now prove that if m and n are integers and $m \neq n$ then $\int_{-\pi}^{\pi} \sin(mx)\cos(nx)dx = 0$. (Hint: expand $\sin(mx+nx)$ and $\sin(mx-nx)$ using two trig identities.)

Between parts A) and B), we have shown that whenever m and n are integers, we have

$$\int_{-\pi}^{\pi} \sin(mx)\cos(nx)dx = 0.$$

It turns out that this fact is just the thing needed to prove that many functions can be written in the form

$$f(x) = \frac{a_0}{2} + a_1\cos(x) + b_1\sin(x) + a_2\cos(2x) + b_2\sin(2x)\cdots$$

where $a_n = \frac{1}{\pi}\int_{-\pi}^{\pi} f(x)\cos(nx)dx$ and $b_n = \frac{1}{\pi}\int_{-\pi}^{\pi} f(x)\sin(nx)dx$.

E) To get a feel for what is involved, use $f(x) = x$ and find a_0, a_1 and b_1.

F) Now, using the methods you used in part E), find the a_n and b_n for $n \geq 1$.

Part F) gives us a rather remarkable way to write the function $f(x) = x$ as a sum of sin and cos functions. This seems like a rather complicated and inconvenient way of expressing a simple function like x, but it turns out that for more complicated functions, (and even $f(x) = x$) this is just the kind of decomposition that we need to answer difficult mathematical questions.

G) (Extra credit) Make and conjecture about what a_n equals when $f(x)$ is an *odd* function. Prove this conjecture.

Appendix C

Mathematics 111   **Information for Students**   **Spring 1994**

<u>Textbook</u>: Stewart, Calculus, Brooks/Cole, 2nd ed. The course will cover nearly all of Chapters 1,2,3,4,6.

<u>Homework</u>: Throughout the semester you will receive lists of suggested exercises to help you learn the material from each section of the text. These exercises indicate what we expect you to be able to do. Work problems until you can do most of them quickly and easily and ALL of them with some effort.

You may need to do even more exercises than we have listed. The book has plenty to choose from. For example, if the suggested exercises are too hard at first, you might need to practice on some easier ones. So go back to the beginning of the exercise set and choose some easier exercises to try. If you continue to have difficulty ask me or consult the Mathematics Support Center, 315 White Hall.

We will also be having regular help sessions as described on another information sheet.

You are also welcome to organize your own study groups in the dorms, etc.

<u>Exams</u>: There will be three prelims and a final. Most of the exam questions will be very much like the suggested exercises, and some may even be taken directly from the exercises (possibly with minor changes). The best way to prepare for the exams is to work problems and work problems and work more problems. It is important to do this as the course goes along. If you start working and studying just a few days before an exam, there is no way you can reach the level you would be at if you had done some each week and then reviewed for the exam.

The prelims, as announced in the catalog, will be at 7:30 p.m. on the following evenings:

Tuesday, February 22
Thursday, March 31
Thursday, April 28

The place of the exam will be announced in class during the week the exam is being held. Those dates were selected by a university committee that tried to avoid conflicts with evening prelims in other large courses. If there are conflicts in spite of this, please let me know well *before the exam* so that I can try to resolve them.

We don't mind giving an exam early or late on the scheduled evening if that helps resolve a conflict. Do not simply fail to show up for an exam and then try to explain why later; you risk an F if you do that.

Mathematics 111   **Regular Study Sessions**   **Spring 1994**

Regular study sessions will be held for any student in Mathematics 111 who wishes to use them. They will be scheduled as follows:

Sunday evenings from 6 to 8 p.m. in room 328, White Hall.

These study sessions should be seen as extensions of your instructor's regular office hours. But the advantage of these sessions is that you can ask for a hint on a problem, work on it further, and get help again without even having to leave the room. Don't ask more than one question at a time. There's no pressure for the instructor to go anywhere.

You can use these study sessions as opportunities to simply come sit and do your math homework, to ask questions and sort out problems you are having, to study with a friend, to make sense of your class notes, to make up for work missed, or to meet whatever your mathematical needs are at the time.

Bring with you your notebooks and homework, possibly a cup of coffee, and maybe a list of problems you've had trouble with. Make yourself comfortable, and begin working.

The room will be staffed by instructors from Mathematics 111 (not necessarily our own instructor). An instructor will come over to you when you want help, and perhaps give you a pointer in the correct direction or help you to understand the objectives of a problem. Then you will be able to work on it further knowing that if you get stuck, help is close at hand.

If you tend not to study regularly, use one of these sessions each week to help you to regulate your math study. If you prefer to study with someone else from time to time, but don't know other students in the course, use these study sessions to put yourself into mathematical circulation. If you prefer to work completely alone, come and do that, knowing that if you need help it is there, immediately, and as briefly as you want it to be.

Appendix D

Math 111: Calculus of a Single Variable
Cornell University Summer Session
June 30 - August 12, 1997

Instructors	Phone	Office	Office Hours	e-mail
Tom Stiadle (Czar)	255-4640	White 408	MWR 10-11	stiadle@math.cornell.edu
Carolyn Desilva	255-8282	White 313	TWR 10-11	cdesilva@math.cornell.edu
G. Odifreddi	255-7559	White 401	MTF 10-11	ogeorge@math.cornell.edu

Teaching Assistants

Swapeel Mahajan	255-9351	White 400	Sun 4-6	swapneel@math.cornell.edu
Suman Ganguli	255-7548	White 327	TR 4-5	suman@math.cornell.edu
Sean Crowe	255-7552	White 499	MW 4:30-5:30	horse@math.cornell.edu

Text: James Stewart, Calculus: Early Transcendentals, 3rd edition, Brooks/Cole 1995.

Prerequisites: This course assumes working knowledge of high school algebra and trigonometry. It is not expected that students have seen calculus before. However, usually several students have studied a little calculus. If you are one of these, do not make the common mistake of trying to "coast" through the course. It will overtake you before you realize it, and there will not be time to catch up.

Content: This course provides an introduction to differential and integral calculus of a single variable. We will cover most of the material in chapters 1, 2, 3, 4 and 5 of the text. Among other things this will include

> Limits of functions - a key idea needed to develop calculus
> Continuity of functions
> Derivatives of functions - rates of change
> Applications of derivatives - graphing functions, optimization
> Integration of functions
> The Fundamental Theorem of Calculus - connecting derivatives and integrals
> Some useful functions

Requirements: The formal course requirements listed below - homework, quizzes exams and class participation - are designed to assist you in mastering the course material. However, you must work every day in order for these activities to make a difference. This is an intense course. You are expected to spend several hours each day outside of class reading, studying and doing problems. It is extremely important not to fall behind in a six week course; there will be no time to catch up. Be sure to ask questions in class or during office hours immediately if you have difficulties. You may go to any of the instructors and teaching assistants for help.

Homework: There are daily reading and problem assignments. You should read the text in order to reinforce the material presented in class. Also, the book contains more examples than will be provided in class. By far the most important activity in the course, though, is the doing of problems. There is an enormous difference between watching an instructor do a problem and doing one yourself. Even the best teacher cannot merely place knowledge in your mind. You must slowly discover it yourself as you struggle with problems. You may work with other students when doing homework, but do not fool yourself by copying another's work. You must be an active participant.

The *'d homework problems will be collected each Monday in class, but you must do all the problems listed.

In addition, several graphing calculator problems will be suggested. Do these to gain more insight if you have such a calculator or can work with someone who does.

Quizzes: There will be ten short quizzes given in class. The problems will resemble recent homework problems.

Exams: There will be two preliminary examinations (prelims) and a final exam. These will determine the bulk of your grade (see below). The best way to prepare is to actually do problems. Do not just "look over" problems; do them.

Prelim 1	Tuesday, July 15	7:30-9:00 pm
Prelim 2	Tuesday, July 29	7:30-9:00 pm
Final	Monday, August 11	8:00-10:30 am

Class Participation: In addition to merely attending class, you are expected to participate in discussions, question-and-answer sessions, and any other classroom activities.

Grading:

Prelims 1 and 2	200 points	40%
Quizzes, Homework, Classwork	150 points	30%
Final Exam	150 points	30%
Total	500 points	100%

Class Schedule and Assignments

Week	Day		Comments	Reading Assignment
1	June 30		Algebra & Trig Review	0.1
	July	1	Quiz #1	0.1,0.2
		2		0.4,1.1
		3	Quiz #2	1.2,1.3
		4	No class-Independence Day	
		7	Homework #1 due	1.3,1.5
2		8	Quiz #3	1.6,1.7
		9		1.7,2.1
		10		2.1,2.2
		11	Quiz #4	2.4,2.5

Homework#	Section	Assigned Problems	Calculator Suggestions
1	0.1	2,4*,18,20,38*,40,48,54,60*, 64,66,67,68,84,88*,99	
	0.2	2,4*,12,24	
	0.4	2*,3,20,22*,25	
	1.1	2*	
	1.2	1,4*,5,8*,16*,18,21a,21b	21c,27,29
	1.3	4,6,12,13,14*,20,24*,16,32,36*	39,40
2	1.3	50,60,62*	
	1.5	2,4*,10,14,22*,29*,34,43,45*,58a	51
	1.6	4,8,14*,24,26*,28,40*,46	35,37
	1.7	2,4,14*,15,18	
	2.1	8,12,14*,26*,32,34,36,40*,52	45,46
	2.2	2,10*,12,18,28,36,38*,46,60*	42,43
	2.4	6,8,14*,20,26,34*,39	35

Appendix E

Mathematics 453   Fall 1999

<u>Instructor</u>: Tom Rishel, Malott 225, 5-3905,rishel@math.cornell.edu

<u>Teaching Assistant</u>: Nelia Charalambous, 101 Malott, 5-7554,nefeli@math.cornell.edu

<u>Text</u>: J. R. Munkres, Topology: A First Course, Prentice-Hall, 1975. We will cover parts of chapters 1-5 and chapter 8.
   Munkres's book is a deceptive one for students, in that he tends to investigate concepts and prove theorems in great detail, thereby making the topics appear reasonably accessible. In actual fact, these concepts were difficult for many professional mathematicians throughout the twentieth century, and are not nearly as easy to grasp as Munkres makes them seem. The exercises in the book are also of a comparable level of difficulty, and should be treated with caution. (I am not trying to scare you away from the book or course, just pointing out that waiting until Thursday evening to try Friday's homework assignment is a very bad idea.)

<u>Course Description</u>: Slightly over half the course will cover what is usually called general topology - topological spaces, separation axioms, continuity, connectedness and compactness, for instance. This material is important for analysis courses, such as Math 413 and 611, and is also the foundation for more advanced work in topology. The later part of the course will offer a general introduction to the algebraic topological ideas of fundamental group and covering space.

<u>Prerequisites</u>: The Cornell catalog lists Math 221 and 411 as prerequisites; it suggests the alternative of "permission of the instructor." I interpret this to mean that "mathematical maturity" is the true prerequisite. Math 453 is a rigorous course that embodies many theorems and proofs, along with a significant number of difficult homework problems. A mature, hard working student who has not had Math 411 can take this course if he or she realizes that the work-level is high, and is willing to expend the effort involved.

<u>Course Requirements and Grading</u>: There will be regular homework assignments, usually problems from the text, due about a week after they are assigned. The homework is a significant aspect of the course, and it will count for about 50% of your grade. Write your solutions clearly and completely; you will be graded on intelligibility of your argument at least as much as you will on your knowing what the core idea of the problem is. It is your responsibility to convince the grader and me that your answer is correct. I will also give an in-class midterm some time in October. The midterm will count for 20% of the grade. A final whose nature will be determined later will also count for 25%. "Class participation," an admittedly ill-defined concept, will account for the last 5% of the grade.

<u>Working Together</u>: I have no objection <u>in principle</u> to your working together, so long as you are really working together. One person's simply telling the others how to do problem is of no value and defeats the purpose of the assignment.

160

Appendix F

Course in College Teaching for Graduate Students
Math 500 - College Teaching - A Seminar

The course will be open to all graduate students, with special emphasis on first-year students. We will meet once a week, for ninety minutes; homework assignments would include readings, sample graded papers and lesson plans, and preparation of case studies for presentation in class. I propose to offer the following six topics, one a week for the first six weeks for the Fall Semester.

Week I - Basics
  Following the syllabus
  How is your TA going?
  Problems? Solutions?
  Case Studies:
    I. You make a mistake. Now what?
    II. You have an obnoxious student. How do you handle that?

Week II - The Structure of Universities
  What do Presidents, Provosts, Deans, etc., do?
  The Professorate + Tenure
  What is the "average life" of a grad student? What have non average grads done?
  Question: Where do you see yourself in ten years? How do you get there?
    What if you don't?

Week III - Grading
  How exams are made; how quizzes are made.
  The specifics of grading last year's first prelim.
  Working together - how to handle different attitudes toward grading;
    regrading questions; cheating; acceding to the instructor's wishes, etc.

Week IV - Jobs
  Jobs you have here at Cornell as a TA.
  Jobs you may have later.
  The basics of getting a job - how the market is constructed. The Teaching Portfolio.

Week V - Writing a CV; writing cover letters. What looks good on a CV?
  Your own course.
  Lesson planning.
  Constructing syllabi and exercises.
  Getting help from others (MSC, LSC, office hours, advising, etc. EARS, etc.).

Week VI - Alternatives to Learning
  Discussions.
  Writing assignments.
  Cooperative learning.
  Project-oriented calculus.

Mechanics: The course will meet once a week, late in the afternoon, for ninety minutes, but only for the first six weeks of the semester. Then, when the semester "gets busy," students will have more time for their other studies. I reserve the possibility of adding one week for "special topics" which I might have forgotten in preparing the above syllabus, but I doubt I will use it.